THE
HEARTY EATER
BOOK

Lesley Waters and Sally Ann Voak

BBC BOOKS

Cover photograph © Paul Moon 1990
Stylist – Kay McGlone
Exercise diagrams © Shirley Soar 1990
All other line illustrations © Patrick Bedeau 1990

Published by BBC Books,
a division of BBC Enterprises Limited,
Woodlands, 80 Wood Lane, London W12 0TT
First published 1990

© Lesley Waters and Sally Ann Voak 1990
ISBN 0 563 21520 8

Set in 11/13 Fournier Roman
Printed and bound in Great Britain by Richard Clay Ltd, Bungay
Cover printed by Richard Clay Ltd, Norwich

CONTENTS

INTRODUCTION   5

EXERCISE: THE HEART OF FITNESS   7
   Ten ways to get moving!   9
   Posture perfect   11
FITTING IN FITNESS   14
KEEP FIT WHILE YOU SIT   18
TEN-MINUTE WORK-OUTS   24
   Fit, active women   24
   Mums with tums   26
   Sporty men   28
   Sagging dads   30
   Teens and twosomes   32
   Stretch your body   34
HOW TO MONITOR YOUR PROGRESS   37

SOUPS   40
MAIN COURSES   51
   Meat   53
   Poultry   60
   Fish   69
   Vegetarian dishes   75
   Salads   86
BAKING   93
PUDDINGS   105
GOODIE BOX   118

HEARTY EATER OUTLETS   123

INDEX OF RECIPES   127

INTRODUCTION

Have you noticed how the pace of life seems to be getting faster these days? No time for a proper meal – just grab another chocolate bar to keep going. And all those traffic jams and cancelled trains – it sends the blood pressure soaring.

But our bodies were built to move around the world on two legs, not four wheels. They begin to creak and complain when the wrong fuel is used and the joints are not lubricated.

In other words, we're eating too much of the wrong food, and taking too little exercise. I know, you've heard it all before – here follows the usual, boring lecture on how we should eat less of the things we enjoy and take uncomfortable exercise when we'd rather watch telly. Well, we can certainly ignore the lectures, but let's not pretend there isn't a risk. Overweight at 30, out of breath at 40, coronary at 50? That's the really gloomy picture. More likely is just having less energy to do the things we enjoy – playing football, taking the kids on an outing, gardening.

So, does it have to be goodbye to the things we like to eat and do? No – but it has to be hello to a new balance. It's really only a touch on the tiller to change course a bit, but that course is for keeps, as the following examples show.

Paul and Robin are truck drivers – they work hard, securing their loads and battling along the motorways. It's a strenuous and stressful job. They're both in their thirties, married with children. A typical day includes four meals – breakfast, lunch and tea on the road and a meal at home in the evening. Robin adores his family but hardly ever saw them as he was asleep in front of the telly by 7.00 pm. Paul was finding his work increasingly difficult as he'd put on five stones in weight since he started driving for a living. Each of them contacted Sally Ann Voak, who invited them to take part in *Bazaar* and gave them the programme's 'Hearty Eater' eating and exercise plan. They were asked to keep a record of the things they ate while they were on the road, and a *Bazaar* cook suggested menus for them and their wives to cook at home. Instead of sweets they took a 'goodie box' in their cabs. As for exercise, Robin took the dog for a walk every day (the dog's fitter too), and Paul worked out in a gym. After ten weeks there was a remarkable difference in each of them. They were slimmer, fitter and felt better. They haven't stopped enjoying a pint in the pub but they no longer pig out on the chips and bangers every day.

Only small changes in their lives, but what a result. And if *they* can do it, with all the temptations of fast food on the road, so can we all.

That's where this book comes in – it's all you need, apart from willpower! It's not a diet book – far from it. But if you use it to plan good eating and exercise habits you'll certainly feel and look slimmer, even if your weight doesn't change. Your family and friends will remark on your energy and get-up-and-go. And there's another bonus – your purse will benefit too. Lesley Waters has devised meals that are low in fat, high in fibre and moderate in calories *and* price.

Remember to plan your day or week to include *all* the meals you'll eat – it's those extra snacks of crisps and chocolate bars which throw the balance, and it's easy to forget how often you've had them. Look in the goodie box section for healthier snacks to eat at home or to take with you to work or on a journey. And don't forget to look out for the Hearty Eater symbol in outlets listed on page 123 when you're eating away from home. You'll see the red smiling heart wherever there are meals which are low in fat, high in fibre and moderate in calories. They are filling, tasty and will give you bags of energy to carry on through the day.

Exercise – whatever it is – *must* fit in with your lifestyle, otherwise you'll never keep it up. Can you walk to the shops, to work, to see friends? Do your journeys take you past a swimming pool? Can you persuade a friend or a member of your family to join you in jogging or working out? Do you enjoy organised games? Read Sally's suggestions – there's bound to be something that fits in with your life.

Above all, have fun both with your food and with fitness. We only live once, so make sure you get the best for yourself and your family. Become a *Bazaar* Hearty Eater!

EXERCISE: THE HEART OF FITNESS

Question: Is exercise good for us? Answer: Yes. Sounds simple and obvious? It should be, but these days getting ENOUGH exercise can be very difficult indeed. The pace of life is such that the opportunities for exercising seem to be few and far between! Despite our crowded roads, most people drive everywhere – for business and for pleasure. More and more people work in sedentary jobs, with machines replacing manual staff, and computers taking over the tedious tasks. When we do get some leisure time, we tend to spend it watching TV, eating or sitting behind the wheel of the car again!

No wonder more and more people are suffering from back trouble, insomnia, digestive problems and – the big killer – heart disease.

Even if you are prepared to put up with the less serious consequences of taking little or no exercise, it simply isn't worth risking your life because you're too busy, lazy or foolish to take care of your body. If that sounds rather tough, it's meant to: heart disease is responsible for one in four deaths in Britain, and accounts for around 60 million days off work each year. You only have one heart, and you owe it to yourself (and your family) to look after it properly.

In this section of *The Hearty Eater Book*, we'll be showing you simple ways of increasing the amount of exercise you take. If you follow our advice, you'll find that it is easy to raise your fitness level without making drastic changes to your lifestyle. The good news is that the lazier you are now, the better you will feel in a few months' time.

Here's what exercise can do for your body and mind:

HEART

If you take the kind of exercise that makes your heart work harder – at least 20 minutes of aerobic exercise (jogging, swimming, cycling), three times a week – you will strengthen your heart. It will be able to pump out more blood when necessary, the arteries will become larger, and it will beat more slowly at rest. Even if you simply walk more, you will increase the supply of blood to your heart. (The term 'aerobic', meaning 'with air', is used to describe any exercise that demands oxygen without causing an intolerable oxygen debt, which means it can be continued for a long period, pushing up the pulse rate. Tennis and squash, for example, are not aerobic because you stop for a 'breather' every time a point is scored.)

There is also evidence that regular exercise helps reduce the amount of cholesterol that is laid down in the walls of the arteries which, again, lessens the chance of a heart attack.

LUNGS

Do you get puffed out when you walk up even a short flight of stairs? Your lungs need 'exercising' too! Most people use only minimum lung capacity in general breathing. If you give your lungs more work to do, they will respond by being more efficient. Breathlessness, tiredness and sleeping difficulties will disappear. You may even find that you recover more quickly from coughs and colds. If you are trying to give up smoking, exercise can help. The craving for nicotine is often triggered by stress, and regular exercise helps beat stress. It is also encouraging to see how your fitness level improves once you stop smoking and this can provide an excellent incentive for kicking the habit once and for all.

BLOOD PRESSURE

Although your blood pressure goes up while you're exercising, it reduces slightly afterwards. If you exercise regularly, after a while your overall blood pressure level will be reduced.

BONES AND JOINTS

Ever suffered from nagging back pain? This is one problem that most of us have experienced, especially if we drive long distances regularly, or work in an office. Exercise can strengthen your bones, preventing back pain and other aches and creaks. Many bone, joint and ligament injuries occur when sudden effort – such as digging the garden, or dashing for a bus – puts unexpected strain on your body. You can beat this by keeping yourself supple and strong. For women, brittle bones can be a real problem in later life. Exercising – even just walking regularly – is one way to prevent this from happening.

WEIGHT

No one ever lost much weight simply by exercising. Even dashing up and down stairs (a good calorie-expending exercise) will only use up around 10 calories a minute. But exercising actually reduces your appetite (not the reverse, as most people think), and it can help you maintain your correct body weight. It also improves your posture and muscle tone – so you LOOK pounds slimmer!

MIND

Stress is one of the major causes of heart disease – and there is no doubt that exercise lowers stress levels. It helps you unwind, calm down, and get rid of tension symptoms like irritability, tiredness, lack of sex drive, loss of sense of humour. So, instead of kicking the cat, cursing other drivers on the motorway or shouting at your family . . . take more exercise!

TEN WAYS TO GET MOVING!

Fit more exercise into your life by making these small adjustments to your daily schedule:

1. Try not to use your car or the bus all the time. If you *have* to drive during working hours, cut out short, unnecessary weekend journeys – to the local shops, for instance. Try parking a few streets away from the shops or get off the bus a few stops earlier. Or buy a folding bike – and drive out into the country for some leisurely exercise!

2. Forget lifts and escalators were ever invented! Walking up several flights of stairs is excellent exercise. Do it briskly, keeping your back straight and taking the strain with your legs.

3.   Plan active weekends. Get your chores done early on Saturday and get out into the country for a long, brisk walk. Don't just watch ice-skating, swimming and soccer on TV – try them! Use your home as a gym: clear the bedroom floor for a jazz-dance work-out.

4.   Walk briskly around the house. Try to be lively when you're fetching things from upstairs, doing housework, tidying up. Wear a tracksuit and trainers if you're at home for the day, put some jazzy pop music on your stereo, and dance through the chores!

5.   Get up ten minutes earlier for a simple work-out. On page 24, you'll find routines suitable for all kinds of people. You'll improve your shape, whip up your circulation, and feel bright-eyed and ready for the day ahead! Don't believe us? Try it and see!

6.   Exercise in unusual places. In bed, in the bath, while you're watching TV! In fact, there is *nowhere* you can't exercise! You can even do some exercises while you stand at a bus-stop or in a lift – without attracting curious glances. See the isometric movements on page 18. (In isometric exercises the muscles are contracted through pushing, pulling, squeezing or pressing against an immovable object. The force of resistance is brought in to act as pressure and the muscles are made to work very hard indeed, promoting strength, tone and endurance without much huffing and puffing!)

7.   Use lunchtimes for exercise. Jog around the park, go to a gym, or dive into a swimming pool. It's more fun than merely sitting down to a cafe or canteen lunch, and you'll feel bright and lively all afternoon.

8.   If you have a dog, take it for long, healthy walks at weekends. Alternatively, 'adopt' a neighbour's pooch.

9.   Go dancing! Whatever your age, it's not too late to learn to boogie. Disco dancing is excellent exercise, and even sedate ballroom dancing will help tone up leg muscles and improve your posture.

10.   Take hearty holidays. Instead of just lounging on the beach for two weeks, use your free time to learn a sport: skiing, wind-surfing, tennis, golf. This kind of holiday is particularly good for those in stressful jobs – you just don't have TIME to worry about work while you're concentrating on staying upright on a ski slope, or sailboard!

POSTURE PERFECT

Ever studied a group of people waiting in a bus queue or supermarket checkout? At least three quarters of them look tired, fed up and irritable – mainly because their posture is absolutely terrible! If you hunch your shoulders, poke your tummy out, stand with one leg twisted around the other, you are *bound* to feel exhausted by the end of the day.

The human body is designed to be an upright machine, and our organs and bones are neatly arranged with that particular plan in mind. If your shoulders sag, your chest will be cramped and your lungs unable to expand fully. So your body cells won't get enough oxygen and you will feel less energetic. If your backbone is not upright, your stomach and intestines will be cramped – leading to wind and tummy aches. If your hip girdle is wobbly, the joints between the backbone and girdle may loosen, causing pain and even arthritis.

Another 'nasty' caused by persistent bad posture is that the body will often try to correct the balance itself by building up pads of flab in funny places: on the thighs, and around the waist, hips and ankles.

So, what is perfect posture? Ideally, your body should be stretched upwards so your backbone is in its natural curves but not held stiffly. Your weight should be evenly balanced on both feet, hip girdle straight, with both hips at the same level. Your buttock muscles should be slightly contracted, tummy held in, shoulders down and back (but not forced), arms held loosely by your side.

If you stand like this, you'll feel comfortable immediately, because your body is being held upright by a very slight contraction of nearly all your muscles, and no one set of muscles is being overworked.

When you walk, keep your toes pointing forwards, and let your arms swing comfortably. If you walk penguin-fashion (most people do), your whole body frame has to adjust to cope. Your toes may become deformed and corns develop. This is also why comfy shoes with plenty of toe room and good arch support are important.

Try to carry as little as possible! Shopping bags, kitbags, heavy briefcases all cause bad posture if carried every day. Instead, aim to travel light with either a shoulder bag with the strap across your body, a light briefcase (swap hands occasionally), or nothing at all!

At the end of every day, do the 10-minute body stretching exercise on page 34, to 'iron out' stresses and strains.

Sitting posture is equally important – whether you're driving, working or watching TV.

IN YOUR CAR

You should be able to drive with your knees comfortably bent (not wedged up under the wheel), shoulders back and down, hands and arms relaxed, and back well supported. The lower part of your back is especially vulnerable, and a small cushion can often help improve on the basic design of your car-seat. Sit well back . . . and make a conscious effort to relax. If you are hunched over the wheel on a long drive, the muscles in the back of you neck will become tense, leading to headaches, and your tummy will flop into Michelin man folds, so your motorway Hearty Eater meal won't be digested properly. Make sure you can see properly – if you have to peer over the wheel or through a dirty windscreen you'll develop a crick in you neck and frown lines!

AT YOUR DESK

Choose a chair which allows you to sit with the surface of your desk or work-bench at elbow height. Or adjust your office chair so it is in this position (and fix it firmly – swivel chairs cause indigestion, swollen ankles and 'executive tummy'!). Sit well back, bottom pressed against the back of the chair, thighs pressed evenly on the seat, making a right angle with the lower part of your legs. Keep your feet flat on the floor – crossed ankles could cause circulation problems, puffiness and even varicose veins. Again, a small cushion at the back of your spine could make all the difference between day-long comfort and nagging pains.

WATCHING TELEVISION

'Flopping' in front of the television is an apt description of most people's favourite leisure-time posture. But, to be fair to your body, it really isn't a good idea to loll on a squashy sofa for four or five hours every night. It is better to sit on a hard, high-backed chair with your bottom well back, feet flat on the floor! If that sounds too formal, sit on the sofa with a cushion behind you, feet flat on the floor. Your knees should not be up under your chin – especially if you like to eat TV dinners without suffering late-night indigestion pains!

IN BED

We spend a third of our lives in bed, so it's worth making sure that the bed we choose is as comfortable as possible. A well-sprung mattress will give more even support to your muscles and limbs than a lumpy or sagging one. If you sink too far into your mattress with one part of your body, the other muscles will have to work overtime to compensate – leading to aches and pains. Mounds of pillows might feel comfortable when you rest you head on them, but, during the night, they'll make you hunch your shoulders and increase your chances of getting a double chin!

LIFTING HEAVY SHOPPING

Always make sure you take the strain on your thighs, not on your back. Thigh muscles are usually underworked, and are tough enough to do the job. So pick up those supermarket bags (two of them, one in each hand, to even out the load), relax your shoulders and stay erect. When you lower the bags onto the floor, bend your knees – not your back! The same rules apply when you are lifting children, picking up a pile of magazines, or getting something from a low shelf.

MOVING FURNITURE

Always *pull* a heavy object, such as a filing cabinet or armchair, rather than pushing it along which inevitably causes strain. Use your legs as leverage, and keep your back straight while you pull. If you are carrying a heavy tray or box of tools, keep it close to your body, with your arms bent, and let your legs take most of the strain. Don't hunch over it.

HOW TO CHECK YOUR POSTURE

Ever caught sight of yourself on one of those security TV screens? Horrifying, isn't it? Before you leave home, check yourself in the mirror – shoulders down, tummy and bottom tucked in. During the day, check your reflection in shop windows and glass doors. If you're sagging, straighten up!

FITTING
IN
FITNESS

Peter and Julie are a young couple in their mid-thirties with two small children. Peter is a sales representative for a large food firm. He drives at least 900 miles a week, eating at motorway cafés along the route.

Julie is housebound for much of the time with a baby son and four-year-old daughter who has just started playschool.

Neither of them takes very much exercise. By the time Peter gets home, he is so exhausted that he just eats a large meal and flops in front of the TV. Julie has promised herself that she will join an aerobics class when the baby starts playschool – but that is three years away! Meanwhile, both are beginning to suffer from the same nagging symptoms: tiredness, insomnia, irritability, breathlessness. And they are both around 1 stone overweight.

How can Peter and Julie introduce simple changes into their lifestyle which will make all the difference to their fitness – bearing in mind that they are living on a fixed, modest income and do not have funds for expensive gym memberships or equipment?

Here are their daily schedules now, with some simple ideas on how they can improve their fitness level:

PETER

7a.m.   Wakes after 8 hours sleep, has breakfast, takes Julie a cup of tea, bathes, dresses, gets in his car and drives to the head office of his company – which is just half a mile away from home.

8.30a.m.   Goes to his office for list of daily appointments. Has quick cup of coffee with his secretary and drives off to first call – a meeting at a company headquarters 20 miles away.

10.30a.m.   Back in the car for a long drive – this time to a factory 100 miles away. The drive takes 2 hours. En route, he stops off for a quick burger and chips lunch in a motorway café.

2p.m.   Peter loads his van with three boxes of new samples and drives off. He is aiming to fit in three short calls this afternoon. One is near a large park, but he is too rushed to take a walk around it. However, he stops off for a coffee and a couple of doughnuts at 4p.m., before driving to his last call, which is approximately 50 miles from home.

6p.m.   He is stuck in a traffic jam – and fuming! A tension headache is making him feel even more irritable. It takes him 2 hours to drive home.

8p.m.   Peter arrives at the housing estate where he lives, but decides to stop off at the pub for a quick drink to calm his nerves.

8.30p.m.   He finally arrives home. He eats dinner with Julie, and then catches up on the news on TV.

11p.m.   Peter goes to bed, totally exhausted.

HOW PETER CAN IMPROVE HIS DAILY ROUTINE:

At the moment, he is spending approximately 7½ hours driving or in meetings, 8 hours asleep, and 2 hours watching TV – that's 17½ hours out of 24 sitting on his bottom or lying down!

Although it is impossible to trim away much of the 7½ hours of driving and meetings, he can certainly fit in more exercise. He can start by setting the alarm for 6.45a.m. and doing a simple workout before he has breakfast.

As the office is only half a mile away from home, he could easily walk there, collect his daily call-sheet and walk home – having his morning cup of coffee with Julie instead of with his secretary, before setting out on his first call of the day.

At lunchtime, he should choose Hearty Eater meals at the motorway café instead of burgers and chips. And he could take time out for a walk, some stretching exercises, or even a jog. If it's raining, he could do simple exercises in the car.

If he takes a healthy mid-afternoon snack of fruit, chilled juice or decaffeinated coffee in the car with him, there is no reason why he can't fit in a walk around a park instead of yet another stopover in a motorway café. He could also use one of the boxes of samples for a simple weight-lifting exercise routine.

Some deep-breathing before his last, longest journey of the day would calm and relax him. During the journey, listening to music on the radio or stereo would help to diffuse the tension.

Why call in at the pub? If he went straight home, he could eat earlier and have more time afterwards for a walk around the block with the dog, or a quick set of exercises (such as those for 'Sagging Dads', page 30) in the garden or bedroom. He could even get rid of the day's frustrations by kicking a ball around for 15 minutes. Before bed, a few 'wind-down' exercises (see page 34) would help unwind the 'knotty bits'!

At weekends, he should spend at least one afternoon swimming with the children, playing soccer, tennis or badminton. And he should also take the children and dog for a long walk – so Julie can have some free time for exercise.

JULIE

7.30a.m.   Gets up after sipping tea in bed. Bathes, and washes baby, feeds him and puts him back in his cot. Wakes Lucie, the couple's four-year-old, washes and dresses her and they both go downstairs for breakfast.

9a.m.   Housework with Lucie 'helping'. Coffee break, then Julie loads the washing machine.

11a.m.   The baby wakes up, is changed and fed. Julie and Lucie play with him in his room, then Julie reads Lucie a story.

12 noon.   Lunch for Julie and Lucie in the kitchen. A friend calls to take Lucie to playschool – which is held in the local church hall.

2p.m.   Julie does the ironing, with baby watching from his special chair.

3p.m.   Julie gets the baby ready and pushes him in his pram to the playschool. They meet Lucie and go to the shops, then to the park for half an hour.

4p.m.   The baby needs changing and feeding, then it's time for Lucie's tea. Julie grabs a couple of biscuits and a cup of tea.

5p.m.   They all watch TV together.

6p.m.   The baby is bathed, changed and fed, then put to bed. Lucie has fun in her bath, then Julie reads to her before tucking her up.

7.30p.m.   More ironing, and Julie catches up with the papers. She prepares a simple evening meal.

8p.m.   Peter is late, so Julie watches TV for a while. They eat together, and watch more TV.

11p.m.   Bedtime. Julie is exhausted.

HOW JULIE CAN IMPROVE HER DAILY ROUTINE:

Julie has hardly any time to herself during the day, but there are periods when she could fit in some exercise. For instance, she could do some stretching movements, such as a yoga routine, when she gets up – before she wakes the children.

Housework is a great opportunity for exercise: stretching to dust high shelves, knee-bends when making the beds, dancing while vacuuming the carpet! Some lively music on the radio would make the session fun, and Lucie would love to join in.

Julie could also take Lucie to playschool and do her shopping afterwards. It is much less stressful to shop with one child in tow than two. On reaching home, the baby would be ready for a nap, and Julie would have an hour to herself for a video exercise session. It would be a good idea to get together with a few friends for a work-out – this would be fun, and stop Julie from being so isolated during the day. Boredom is a major cause of tiredness.

If Julie wore a tracksuit and took a ball or skipping ropes when she went to fetch Lucie from playschool, they could both have a lot of fun in the park – while the baby watches from his pram!

Watching TV with the children would be a good opportunity for some floor or chair exercises.

When they are safely tucked up in bed, Julie could do some skipping, jogging on the spot, or simple exercises in the kitchen, and have a reviving bath before Peter comes home.

KEEP FIT
WHILE YOU SIT

It isn't always possible to exercise in a gym, or outdoors. But, we ALL have time to do some simple exercises when we're sitting down – watching TV, in a parked car, at work. In fact, sitting exercises are far more useful in a keep-fit programme than most people think. They can help tone up the upper body, bottom and thighs. They are particularly good for beating shoulder strain (which can lead to headaches), and lower back pain. Harrassed sedentary workers who suffer from stress-related problems can benefit too – for body tension is one of the main results of stress. A five-minute break for some simple de-tensing movements can help a great deal when you are under pressure.

With practice, a lot of the exercises below become automatic. Most are fairly unobtrusive, so you won't disturb your family, fellow workers or drivers with your strange antics! Many of them are also excellent for anyone confined to a wheelchair – but, if you are disabled, do check with your doctor before you do this or any other keep-fit programme.

Some of the movements we have included are isometric. The principle of isometrics is simple: the muscle is contracted through pushing, pulling, squeezing or pressing against an immovable object. The force of resistance acts as pressure and the muscle is made to work very hard – promoting strength, tone and endurance without the amount of effort that exercises with vigorous movements require.

AT WORK

Try these exercises while you're sitting at your desk (they can also be adapted for home use – sitting at the kitchen table, perhaps). First, make sure you are in the correct sitting position: sit well back, with your bottom pressed against the back of the chair, thighs pressed evenly on the seat. There should be an angle of 90° between your thighs and the lower part of your legs, behind your knees. Your feet should be flat on the floor, with another 90° angle between feet and shins. Hold your backbone upright, but not ramrod stiff, and relax your shoulders. And keep your tummy in, too.

1.   FOR UPPER ARMS

Sit with your back straight, feet together. Place the palms of your hands on the desk or table in front of you. Press down as hard as you can, as if you were trying to force the desk down. Hold the position for a count of six. Relax. Now put your hands underneath, palms up, elbows tucked in. Push upwards hard, again for a count of six. Relax. Repeat five times.

2.   FOR INSIDE THIGH MUSCLES

Sit with your back straight, feet together. Now place a strong object, such as a metal wastepaper bin, tough briefcase or large saucepan, between your feet. Squeeze your feet together as hard as possible for a count of six, then relax. Your should feel your inside thigh muscles working quite hard. Repeat five times.

3.   FOR CHEST

Again, sit with your back straight, feet together. Tuck your elbows in by your sides and place the palms of your hands against a strong object on the desk in front of you, such as a word-processor keyboard, typewriter, or metal wastepaper bin. Push hard. (You should see your bosom 'jump' slightly if you are a woman.) Hold the position for a count of six, then relax. Repeat five times.

4.   FOR TUMMY

In the same sitting position, relax your shoulders and place your hands near the back of your chair, grasping the chair-seat firmly. Now inhale and lift your pelvis, so the pubic bone rises, but your bottom stays on the seat – in a rolling movement. The curve of your lower spine will straighten and your tummy will be compressed. Hold the position briefly, then exhale. Repeat six times. This one is particularly good for women who need to tighten up their tummy muscles after having a baby because it is gentle.

5. FOR BOTTOM

Sit comfortably, hands resting on your thighs. Now contract your thigh and buttock muscles, and roll your thighs outwards slightly. Hold for a count of three, relax. Repeat 20 times for a really excellent bottom-tightening routine which no one can see!

6. FOR SHOULDER TENSION

Sit with your feet slightly apart, hands on your knees. Now relax your shoulders. Roll your right shoulder back for a count of three, then forward for another count of three. Repeat with left shoulder, then both together.

IN YOUR CAR

On a long journey, exercising is essential to prevent tension headaches, indigestion and general fatigue. It is obviously dangerous to exercise while you are driving along (stop in a layby), but you can check on your body position while you are at a red light or caught in a jam. Make a conscious effort to relax your shoulders, arms and chest, pull in your tummy muscles if they're sagging, and wind down the window so you can take a breather.

When you pull into that layby or café carpark, try this simple routine:

1. FOR SHOULDER TENSION

Sit with your back straight, hands clasped loosely behind you with your elbows slightly bent. Now, draw your shoulder blades together and push your upper arms together without trying to straighten your elbows. Repeat six times.

2. FOR POSTURE, SHOULDERS

Sit straight, feet together, with the palms of your hands on your lower ribcage, just above your waistline. Now push your elbows and upper arms backwards towards your spine in sharp, short jerks – about six altogether. Relax, and repeat six times.

3. FOR WAISTLINE

Sit straight, palms of your hands on your upper chest, elbows out. Now lift your breastbone and ribcage and twist your torso and head around to the left as far as you can. Keep your pelvis static. Try to push your body just a little bit more with a short, sharp movement. Repeat the whole exercise five times to the left, five to the right.

4. FOR CHEST, UPPER ARMS

Sit straight, hands holding the steering wheel at the '9 o'clock' and '3 o'clock' position. Make sure your knees are slightly apart, feet flat on the floor. Push your hands sharply against the steering wheel, hold the position for a count of six, and then relax. Repeat ten times.

5. FOR TUMMY

Sitting comfortably, shoulders relaxed, bottom well back in your seat, take a deep breath. Now lift your ribcage, and exhale through your mouth, pulling in your tummy at the same time (aim to touch your backbone with your navel!). Hold for a count of three, inhale and let your tummy expand again. Repeat ten times.

6. FOR BOTTOM

Place your hands on the car-seat by your sides, palms down. Now press down, and raise your bottom off the seat slightly. Contract your buttock muscles hard, hold for a count of six, then relax. Repeat six times.

WATCHING TV

Sitting down watching TV is the perfect time for exercising! You are in the same place for an hour or two, and there are no distractions apart from the programme being shown on your set. As you are at home, you can try fairly vigorous movements which might look out of place in your office, or in your car!

If you practise the routine below, you will soon be able to do it without consulting this book. Hopefully, exercising will soon become a regular part of your evening's viewing!

Your best exercise 'hot seat' is a straight-backed chair with a firm seat. Sit well back, shoulders relaxed, arms by your sides, and hold your tummy in. Now try these:

1. FOR ARMS, SHOULDERS

Sit forward in your seat, and make sure you are well away from ornaments, vases and fellow viewers. Now swing your left arm up and backwards in a circle, keeping it as close to your ear as possible (don't poke your head forward). Repeat ten times, then ten times with the other arm.

2. FOR TUMMY

Hold the seat of your chair with your hands. Pull in your tummy and straighten your arms so you pull yourself up out of the chair, breathing out as you do so. You must keep your back straight and your shoulders relaxed. If you can, raise your knees towards your chest. Breathe in as you return to the first position. Repeat five times.

3. FOR CHEST

Sit with your arms out at shoulder level, elbows slightly bent, palms facing forwards. Now clench your fists and bring your arms forwards so they cross over in front of your face. Press a little bit further, then return to the starting position. Repeat, criss-crossing at shoulder level, then at chest level, for a count of 20.

4. FOR WAIST AND TUMMY

Sit with your tummy in, back straight, ribcage raised, shoulders relaxed. Now clasp your hands straight above your head, with your elbows out. Check your posture. Bend to the right as far as possible, keeping your bottom on the chair. Hold for a count of three, then raise your body slightly and bend a little further. Come back to the starting position and bend to the other side. Repeat ten times.

5. FOR BOTTOM AND THIGHS

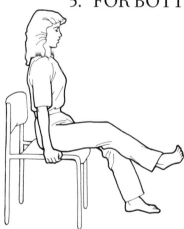

Sit forward, hands on your waist, back straight. Raise your pubic bone, and lift your bottom slightly, straightening out the natural hollow in your back. Turn your thighs outwards and lift your right leg, with your knee slightly bent, foot bent upwards. Straighten the leg, pushing your heel away from you. Do six more 'kicks', then repeat with the other leg.

6. FOR FEET, ANKLES, TUMMY

Sit straight, tummy well in, and raise your left foot off the ground, without bending your knee. Now circle your foot 20 times to the right, 20 times to the left. Repeat with your other leg.

TEN-MINUTE WORK-OUTS

It takes just 10 minutes a day to transform a tired, sagging body into a lively, shapely one. That's all the time you need for a simple, effective work-out which you can fit in before breakfast, or during your lunch-break.

But you must do your work-out every single day! Some bouncy music on the radio or stereo will get you in the mood. Wear a loose tracksuit – NOT tight-fitting jeans! – with bare feet or training shoes.

Here are five super programmes for very different people:

FIT, ACTIVE WOMEN

Leap into action every day with this easy routine. It's good for young women, and older ones who've stayed in fairly good shape. It is also fun with young children joining in or just watching.

1. WARM-UP

Stand with your feet apart, back straight, and a light weight (such as a can of baked beans) in each hand. Stretch your hands above your head. Now swing your arms forwards and down between your legs, bending your knees but keeping your back straight. Straighten your legs and swing your arms back up above your head. It's important to breathe in as you stretch up, breathe out as you curl down. Repeat ten times.

2. WAIST

Now put down the weights. Clasp your hands in front of your face, elbows out (your feet should still be apart). Keeping your body straight, raise your right heel and twist to the left as far as possible, then raise your left heel and twist to the right. Repeat 20 times.

3. TUMMY

Lie on your back, with your feet on the floor, knees bent and legs slightly apart. Now raise your arms to knee level, hands together, fingers straight. Leading with your head, and using your tummy muscles, roll up your back to a sitting position. Go as far as you can with your arms thrusting through your knees. Slowly, roll down, head going down last. N.B. It is very important to use your tummy muscles to lift your body – don't take the strain with your back. Repeat five times.

4. THIGHS AND BOTTOM

Still lying on the floor, stretch your arms out level with your shoulders, palms down. Point your toes, and place your feet together, with legs straight. Now raise your right leg as high as you can, keeping it straight. Flex the foot towards you, and cross the leg over to touch the floor on your left, as high as you can. (Don't raise your shoulders off the floor, or twist your body.) Repeat with the other leg. Repeat the whole movement five times.

5. BUST

Stay on the floor, but grab those baked beans tins again, one in each hand. Now, with legs straight and feet together, stretch your arms out at right angles to your body. Keeping your arms straight, fling them across your chest, then out to each side in a 'scissors' movement. Repeat 10 times.

6. STAMINA

Up onto your feet now, for a bit of 'jogging'. Run on the spot for a count of 30!

MUMS WITH TUMS

This controlled work-out will help streamline your shape (but you'll need to watch your eating too – try the sensible recipes in this book).

1. POSTURE STRETCH

Stand straight, with your feet slightly apart. Now raise your arms above your head and go up on your toes. Pull in your tummy muscles, contract your buttocks and raise your pubic bone so that your pelvis is tilted forwards and upwards. Now raise your breastbone to elongate your ribcage. Count three, and lower your heels. Repeat once.

2. WAIST

Stand with your feet about 2 feet apart, hands by your sides, body stretched up. Now raise your right arm above your head and bend your body, from the waist only, over to the left as far as you can go. Straighten up and repeat to the right. It's important to keep your body straight – don't lean forwards. Repeat six times on each side.

3. HIPS, LEGS

Stand facing a chair or sofa back, which should be at waist level. Place your hands on it for balance, shoulders level, body upright, and raise your left leg to the side, then swing it down across your right leg and up again. Repeat ten times, then ten times with your left leg. Turn sideways-on to the chair back, raise your outside leg in front of your body, relax it and swing it down and back (don't lean forward). Repeat ten times, then turn round and repeat ten times with the other leg.

4. BUST

Stand with your feet about 2 feet apart, raise your arms straight out on each side to shoulder height and bend your elbows so that your left fist is slightly higher than the right and thus level with your right elbow. Now move your elbows in and out so that your fists make rapid 'crossover' movements in front of your chest. Repeat 20 times, keeping your arms at shoulder height.

5. BOTTOM, THIGHS

Lie on your tummy on the floor, hands by your sides, palms down. Rest your head comfortably on one side. Now, keeping your legs straight, raise your right leg as high as possible, cross it over your left leg and lower to touch the floor. Raise, then lower to the starting position. Repeat with the left leg, this time crossing over your right leg. Repeat the whole movement five times.

6. SPINE, SHOULDERS, TUMMY

Still on your tummy, feet together, toes pointed, place your hands on the floor at shoulder level, palms down. Now straighten your arms slowly, to raise the top half of your body off the floor. Look up at the ceiling, then lower your body slowly. Repeat twice.

SPORTY MEN

It's better to find time for a daily work-out than play squash, golf or soccer once or twice a week. Remember: sudden exercise is bad news – you *must* do a few stretching exercises before your game. This set of movements gives you a head-to-toe stretch-and-tone. Use it as a pre-match warm-up before your game, as well as a daily routine.

1. LEGS AND ARMS

Stand straight with your feet together, hands by your sides. Now step back with your left foot, keeping your weight forwards, and your left heel off the ground. Raise your right arm above your head. Raise your left leg and push your right arm back, still keeping your right leg straight. Repeat six times, then six times with the right leg, left arm.

2. WAIST

Stand straight with feet about 3 feet apart, hands by your sides. Now raise your arms straight above your head and clasp your hands, with the palms down. Keeping your arms straight, lean to the left from the waist, as far as you can without leaning forwards or moving your feet. Return to the starting position, then lean to the right. Repeat ten times.

3. TUMMY

Lie on your back, feet together. Sit up slightly, supporting yourself on your elbows. Bend your knees and lift your feet up off the floor. Stretch out your legs and lower them to a point as near as possible to the floor without flopping. Bend your knees again, raise your feet, then lower them to the same point. Repeat five times.

4. BOTTOM, HIPS

Kneel on the floor on all fours, placing your hands at shoulder level with the fingers pointing forwards. Stretch your right leg out to one side, foot pointing forwards. Now raise this leg as high as you can, keeping it at right angles to your body. After five repetitions, repeat with your left leg.

5. CHEST

Still kneeling, place your hands flat on the floor in front of you, elbows straight, fingers pointing forwards, back straight. Now raise your feet, ankles crossed. Bend your elbows and lower your body slowly, so that your chin touches the ground in front of you. Straighten your arms, raising your body to the starting position. Repeat five times, increasing to ten with practice!

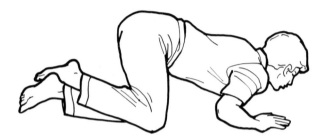

6. STAMINA

Stand up now and jog on the spot for 30 'paces'.

SAGGING DADS

Don't despair if your bulging tum and wobbly waistline are spoiling your manly figure. These exercises, plus a sensible eating plan, will help you shape up.

1. SHOULDERS, CHEST, POSTURE

Stand with your feet very wide apart, back straight, arms by your sides. Swing your arms up in front of you (keeping them straight) until they are level with your shoulders. Then swing them out sideways and return to the starting position. Repeat ten times in a very smooth, continuous movement.

2. WAIST

In the same standing position, place your hands on your hips. Now bend to the left, keeping your back and body straight, then bend to the right without jerking. Repeat ten times.

3. LEGS

Stand with your right leg forward, left leg behind. Both legs should be straight and feet flat on the floor. Put your hands on your hips. Now bend your right knee, moving your weight onto it. Keep your back straight and go down as low as you can without leaning forward. Repeat five times, swap legs and repeat a further five times.

4. TUMMY, SPINE

Legs wide apart now, hands by your sides. Take a breath and, as you breathe out, bend forward from the waist and thrust your hands though your legs, palms down, as far as they will go without straining. Breathing in, raise your body, place your hands on your waist and lean back slightly. Repeat five times.

5. BOTTOM

Stand facing a wall, arms' distance away, with the palms of your hands flat against it. Now raise your right knee to your chest, then stretch the leg down and swing it up and backwards as high as you can. Keep it straight, and don't lean forwards. Repeat five times, then swap legs and repeat a further five times.

6. STAMINA

On your hands and knees on the floor, stretch out your right leg, leaving your left knee as near your chest as possible. Alternate left and right legs in a 'running' movement on the spot. Do six paces with each foot, increasing to 12 as your stamina improves!

TEENS AND TWOSOMES

These exercises are great fun because they are designed to be done by two people together. So they are very suitable for couples, young people and anyone who wants to have some fun while they work out. It doesn't matter if your partner is taller or shorter than you.

1. WARM-UP

Stand facing each other, holding hands, backs straight. Now 'scissor' your feet, forwards and backwards for a count of ten.

2. LEGS

Still facing your partner, holding hands, place your feet slightly apart. Now, keeping your backs straight, heels on the ground, go down into a knees-bend together. Go just as far as the weaker member of the twosome can manage, then straighten up. Repeat six times.

3. TUMMY

Lie on the floor with your knees bent, feet about 2 feet apart, and hands by your sides. Get your partner to kneel in front and hold your ankles as an 'anchor'. Raise your arms and upper body and try to thrust your hands through your knees, using your tummy muscles to lift your body. Repeat five times, swap over and repeat.

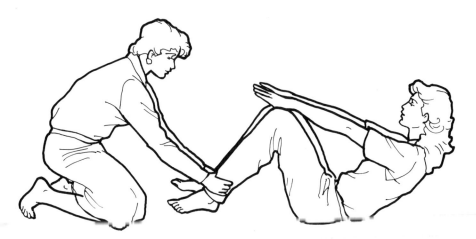

4. WAIST

Now, up on your feet again for 'twists'. Face each other, holding hands, feet together, knees slightly bent. Twist your lower body in opposite directions, first to the left, then to the right. Keep it up for a count of 20.

5. BACK, LEGS

Sit facing each other, holding hands, with your legs widespread and your feet braced against each other's feet. If one partner is shorter, he or she should rest their feet against their partner's calves. Now with backs erect, lean backwards, and forwards – the partner leaning backwards should give a steady, non-jerky movement, while the other partner relaxes forwards. Repeat for ten 'see-saws'.

6. BOTTOM, THIGHS

Standing facing each other and holding hands for balance, one partner should kick his or her left leg up, leaning forwards slightly, while the other kicks his or her left leg up, leaning backwards slightly. Repeat ten times with each leg.

STRETCH YOUR BODY

One of the hazards of modern living is that we twist and torture our bodies into unnatural positions for much of the time. Just think about it for a moment: you get up, after having a lovely stretch in bed, and do some exercises (so far, terrific!). Then, you spoil it all by spending the rest of the day hunched up in your car or office, standing on one leg in a crowded train, or squashed up against other drinkers in a wine bar or pub! No wonder it's been estimated that we end up a few centimetres shorter at the end of the day.

Of course, the human body is designed to cope with such indignities, but you can help it cope better if you do some stretching exercises every night. They will help you to unwind and improve the flexibility of your muscles and joints. This means that you will be less susceptible to soreness, cramp and minor injuries like pulled muscles, sprained ankles and wrenched elbows. If you are feeling tired and irritable after the day's physical and mental strains, the exercise will also help to calm and relax you. They are also brilliant for improving your digestion! Try the programme below. It is based on simple, controlled movements which are inspired by classic yoga poses.

Make sure you do your exercises in a warm room, on a soft carpet or rug. They take up very little space, so the bedroom is ideal. Strip off your constricting daytime clothes, and do them wearing a loose tracksuit or just your undies. Bare feet are essential.

1. COMPLETE STRETCH

This exercise helps to take the tension out of your arms, back and legs. It also strengthens your tummy muscles. Stand with your feet together, arms above your head, fingers clasped loosely. Look up at your hands. Bend your knees and bring your hands down slowly to the horizontal position. Let your hands fall sideways and down, and relax your head forward. Pause, then reverse the movement. Repeat five times. Breathe in as you raise your body, out as you lower it.

2. 'CAT' EXERCISE

This exercise stretches your spine, shoulder and neck muscles. Kneel on the floor and place your hands on the floor in front of your shoulders' width apart. Your knees should be together, feet stretched out. Hollow your back and look up at the ceiling. Count five, then arch your back, letting your head hang down. Count five and repeat the whole movement five times. Breathe in as you hollow your back, out as you arch it.

3. BACKWARD BEND

This removes tension and stiffness from your toes, feet, ankles and neck, and firms up tummy and chest. Sit on your heels, with knees together, hands behind you for balance. Slowly move your hands back to a comfortable distance behind you. Now raise your upper body to form an arch, dropping your head back, but staying in the same sitting position. Slowly relax your upper body, pause and repeat five times. Breathe in as you raise your body, out as you relax it.

4. HIP SWING

This exercise increases thigh and hip mobility. Sit on the floor, hands behind you for support, back straight, knees bent, shoulders relaxed. Now push your hips over to the right, lowering your knees to touch the floor. Repeat to the left. Repeat the complete movement five times. Breathe regularly throughout this exercise.

5. ARM AND LEG STRETCH

This exercise relieves tension in back, shoulders and legs and helps improve posture and balance. Stand straight with your right side against a wall or the side of the bed for balance. Raise your right arm overhead, with your elbow straight. Now raise your left leg backwards, and hold it with your left hand. Slowly, bring your right arm and head back and gently pull your left foot upwards towards your back. Don't strain. Relax and rest for a moment, standing perfectly still. Now swap sides and repeat the movements – this time raising your left arm and right leg. Breathe regularly throughout.

6. SHOULDER STAND

This exercise improves blood circulation and relaxes the legs. Lie on your back, arms by your sides. Let your body go completely limp. With the palms of your hands pressing down against the floor, slowly raise your legs, keeping them straight. Pushing down hard, lift your waist and hips from the floor and prop your hands against your back for support. Slowly correct your balance so your legs are as near to the vertical position as you can make them. Close your eyes and concentrate on slow, rythmical breathing for a few moments, then lower your legs to the floor without thumping! Breathe out as you raise your legs, in as you lower them.

HOW TO MONITOR YOUR PROGRESS

If you take all the advice in this book, you *will* get fitter – and that's a promise. However, there are ways you can check whether your exercise campaign is really working. Here's how:

1. CHECK YOUR PULSE

Once you start to exercise regularly, one of the best ways to find out if you are getting fitter is to take your own pulse before you exercise and again a minute or two after you have finished exercising. There are two changes which you should take notice of. Firstly, as you progress in fitness, the number of beats per minute of your 'resting' pulse should decrease. Secondly, your pulse should return to normal more quickly after exercise – within a minute or two if you are pretty fit.

What is a good 'resting' pulse rate to aim for? If it registers below 60 beats per minute in a man, or 70 in a woman, he or she is likely to be fit. If it is over 90 in a man, or 100 in a woman, he or she is likely to be unfit.

Here's how to check your pulse: you need a watch or clock with a second hand. Put it on the table in front of you so you can see it clearly. Now place the first two fingers of your right hand on the underside of your wrist, about ¼ inch (5 mm) in from the thumb side of your arm. Don't press hard, just let your fingers rest there lightly. When you have located the pulse, count the number of beats for 15 seconds. Multiply by four to get the correct number of beats per minute.

2. SET YOURSELF FITNESS TESTS

Use an everyday physical task as a mini work-out so that you can judge your own fitness. It could be a flight of stairs at work that you climb regularly, a stretch of pavement you walk along each day on your way to the bus-stop, a couple of bags of heavy shopping that you carry regularly from the supermarket to the car-park. Check how breathless and tired you feel at the end of each task. If you are doing your exercises correctly, you should find yourself running up those stairs two at a time without being puffed out, jogging to the bus-stop, and holding those bags so easily that they feel much less heavy than usual. No? Carry on exercising!

You can also try this test which was devised to check the progress of a group of heart patients who embarked on a physical training course:

Choose a step about 8 inches (20 cm) high, and then step up and down onto it briskly at the rate of 24 times a minute for 3 minutes (practise first for 30 seconds to get your pacing right).

Now rest for 1 minute, then check your pulse against the table below to see how fit you are:

UNDER 40

Men	Women	Score
Less than 70	Less than 78	excellent
70–80	78–89	good
81–98	90–110	not bad
More than 99	More than 111	poor

OVER 40

Men	Women	Score
Less than 74	Less than 82	excellent
74–84	82–92	good
85–102	93–114	not bad
More than 103	More than 115	poor

3. LOOK FOR THESE POSTIVE HEALTH SIGNS:

● More energy. You seem to be able to pack more fun into your day. Routine tasks don't seem as tedious, you are always ready to go out on the town, play sports, meet new people.

● Better sleep pattern. Instead of tossing and turning all night, you go to sleep as soon as your head hits the pillow. You wake up refreshed, not tired.

• Fewer minor ailments. You seem to catch fewer colds, be less prone to aches and pains than before.

• Less risk of major ailments. You minimise your chances of heart disease, respiratory problems, high blood pressure, and osteoporosis. If you do have to undergo surgery, or are hospitalised for any reason, you'll recover faster.

• Improved looks. People comment that you look younger, more vital these days. Your skin seems clearer, your body firmer.

• Less stress. You cope better with pressure, at work and at home. You plan your time more efficiently, tackle tasks more positively, deal with minor irritations without losing your temper. Your family remark that you are easier to live with!

SOUPS

TIPS

A thick delicious soup makes an excellent hearty filler which is inexpensive and easy to prepare. Forget the idea of soup as a starter and use it as part of your main meal.

- For smooth soups, cut the vegetables small so that they cook faster.

- Soup can be made with water – stock is not necessary. However, if you are using stock cubes, use sparingly as they are very strong.

- Make good use of the herbs and spices now readily available: they will add character and body to your soups.

- Simmer rather than boil your soups and you will achieve a better result.

- If, during cooking, your soup suffers excessive evaporation, just add extra water or stock.

- Freeze any left-over soup or use as a sauce to accompany pasta.

- Thicken soups by adding grated potatoes.

- Garnish your soups with extra vegetables, seeds or herbs, or try adding cooked brown rice or pasta.

PASTA SOUP

SERVES 4

1 tablespoon sunflower oil
1 onion, chopped
1 clove garlic, crushed
4 oz (100 g) lean bacon, chopped
2 sticks celery, chopped
1 teaspoon dried basil
1/2 teaspoon dried thyme
1/2 oz (15 g) plain flour
1 × 14 oz (400 g) tin chopped tomatoes
4 oz (100 g) small wholemeal pasta shapes
About 2 pints (1.2 litres) vegetable stock
Freshly ground black pepper
1 × 14 oz (400 g) tin red kidney beans, drained
6 oz (175 g) green or *runner beans, chopped*
2 oz (50 g) Edam cheese, grated
2 tablespoons chopped parsley

- This chunky soup really is a meal. You can omit the meat or use some diced chicken flesh as an alternative.

Heat the oil in a pan and add the onion and garlic. Cover with a lid and cook gently for 2 minutes. Remove the lid and stir in the bacon, celery and herbs, cover again and cook for 3 minutes.

Sprinkle over the flour and add the tomatoes, pasta, stock and pepper. Bring to the boil and simmer gently for 20 minutes.

Put in the kidney and green or runner beans and cook for a further 12 minutes, adding extra stock if needed. Sprinkle the soup with the grated cheese and chopped parsley and serve.

LEEK, CARROT & OATMEAL SOUP

SERVES 4

1 tablespoon sunflower oil
1 onion, chopped
1 lb (450 g) leeks, sliced
1 clove garlic, crushed (optional)
Freshly ground black pepper
2 oz (50 g) medium oatmeal or porridge oats
1½ pints (900 ml) vegetable stock or water
10 fl oz (300 ml) semi-skimmed milk
3 tablespoons chopped parsley
4 oz (100 g) carrots, washed and grated

• This warming, welcoming soup has a lovely oaty flavour. It's great on a cold winter's day – when on the road, look out for a Hearty Eater soup like this one. Serve it with warm oatcakes or granary bread.

Heat the oil in a large saucepan and add the onion, leeks, garlic and pepper. Cover and cook over a medium heat for 3 minutes (this will help soften the vegetables). Add half the oatmeal or porridge oats and stir well. Stir in the vegetable stock or water and bring to the boil. Cover and simmer for 20 minutes.

Toast the remaining oatmeal or oats on a baking sheet in the oven at gas mark 7, 425°F (220°C), or in a dry frying-pan on top of the stove, until lightly browned.

Purée the cooked soup in a liquidiser, then return to the saucepan. Add the milk and half the parsley and stir in the grated carrot. Season to taste. Bring the soup back to the boil and simmer for 2 minutes. Sprinkle over the toasted oatmeal or oats and remaining chopped parsley before serving.

POTATO, BACON & GARLIC CHOWDER

SERVES 4

2 cloves garlic, crushed
1½ lb (750 g) potatoes, peeled and chopped
1 bay leaf
1 teaspoon ground turmeric
1½ pints (900 ml) vegetable stock
Freshly ground black pepper
8 oz (225 g) frozen sweetcorn
4 oz (100 g) lean smoked bacon, rinded, grilled and chopped
5 fl oz (150 ml) semi-skimmed milk
2 tablespoons chopped parsley

● Another soup which is a meal in itself. Serve it with warm granary rolls and plenty of freshly ground black pepper.

Place the garlic, potatoes, bay leaf and turmeric in a large saucepan. Pour in the stock and add black pepper. Cover the pan, bring the contents to the boil and simmer for 25–30 minutes or until the potatoes are tender.

Remove the bay leaf and liquidise the soup until smooth. Return to the saucepan and add the sweetcorn, bacon and milk. Simmer, uncovered, for a further 5–10 minutes. Stir in the parsley. Taste and adjust the seasoning if necessary before serving.

SPICED LENTIL HOTPOT

SERVES 4

4 oz (100 g) green split peas
4 oz (100 g) red lentils
1 tablespoon sunflower oil
1 leek, finely sliced
1 clove garlic, crushed (optional)
2 sticks celery, chopped
2 teaspoons ground turmeric
2 teaspoons ground coriander
About 2 pints (1.2 litres) vegetable stock or *water*
Freshly ground black pepper
Grated rind and juice 1 orange
4 tablespoons natural yoghurt

● You don't need to soak red lentils, so this dish takes no time at all to cook. Follow it with a large bowl of crisp salad. Look out of this type of high-fibre filling soup at one of the Hearty Eater restaurants

Wash and pick over the split peas and lentils. Heat the oil in a saucepan, add the leek, garlic (if using) and celery, cover with a lid and let the vegetables cook gently in their own juices for 2 minutes

Remove the lid and add the spices, stir well and cook for a further 3 minutes, uncovered. Add the peas, lentils, vegetable stock or water and black pepper and stir well. Bring to the boil and simmer, uncovered, for 35 minutes or until the pulses are soft. Add extra stock or water if needed during cooking.

Stir in the orange rind and juice. Taste the soup and adjust the seasoning if necessary. Serve in soup bowls with a spoonful of natural yoghurt and a grinding of fresh black pepper.

SPICY BAKED BEAN SOUP

SERVES 4

1 tablespoon sunflower oil
1 onion, chopped
1 clove garlic, crushed
2 sticks celery, finely chopped
2 teaspoons ground coriander
1 level teaspoon chilli powder
2 tablespoons tomato purée
1 × 8 oz (225 g) tin chopped tomatoes
10 fl oz (300 ml) vegetable stock
Freshly ground black pepper
1 × 1 lb (450 g) tin baked beans in tomato sauce

TO FINISH THE SOUP:

3 tomatoes, chopped
Juice 1 lemon

● This store-cupboard soup is cheap, filling and very tasty. If you haven't got all the spices to hand, just use extra black pepper or curry powder. Serve with tortilla chips or wholemeal pitta bread stuffed with crisp bean sprouts.

Heat the oil in a large saucepan and fry the onion, garlic and celery. Add the ground coriander and chilli powder and cook for 30 seconds. Add the tomato purée, tinned tomatoes, stock and black pepper. Stir well.

Bring the contents of the pan to the boil, cover with a lid, lower the heat and simmer for 20 minutes. Stir in the beans in tomato sauce and cook for a further 10 minutes. Taste and adjust the seasoning as necessary.

Pour the soup into warmed soup bowls and sprinkle with the chopped fresh tomatoes and a little lemon juice.

MUSHROOM, THYME & BROWN BREAD SOUP

SERVES 4

1 tablespoon sunflower oil
1 medium onion or 1 bunch spring onions, chopped
8 oz (225 g) large flat mushrooms, washed and sliced
1 clove garlic, crushed
1 level teaspoon dried thyme
2 slices wholemeal bread, broken into pieces
1 pint (600 ml) vegetable stock
10 fl oz (300 ml) semi-skimmed milk
Freshly ground black pepper
3 tablespoons chopped parsley

● Next time you are in a Hearty Eater restaurant, look out for the home-made soup of the day. Mushrooms always give a lovely flavour to any dish, and the brown bread is used to help thicken the soup. Serve with warm crusty wholemeal rolls or a baked jacket potato filled with salad.

Heat the oil in a saucepan, add the onion or spring onions, sliced mushrooms, garlic and thyme. Cook over a medium heat for 5 minutes.

Add the bread pieces, stock, milk and black pepper. Bring to the boil and simmer, uncovered, for 20 minutes.

Liquidise the soup until smooth, return to the saucepan and re-heat until piping hot. Stir in the parsley and taste to check the seasoning, adjusting it as necessary. Serve at once.

PUMPKIN & NUTMEG BROTH

SERVES 4

2 lb (1 kg) pumpkin
10 fl oz (300 ml) water
1 bay leaf
½ teaspoon ground nutmeg
Freshly ground black pepper
1 pint (600 ml) semi-skimmed milk
2 thick slices wholemeal bread, toasted and cut into chunks

● Pumpkin is at its cheapest in the autumn when it's in season. This soup is very cheap to make and really heart-warming.

Cut the pumpkin in half, take out the seeds and reserve. Using a spoon, scoop out the orange flesh; alternatively, use a knife to cut the skin carefully away from the flesh. Dice the flesh and put it into a saucepan with the water, bay leaf, nutmeg and pepper. Simmer for 15–20 minutes or until really soft.

Meanwhile, wash and dry the pumpkin seeds and toast them in the oven at gas mark 7, 425°F (220°C), or in a dry pan over a high heat, until crisp. Set aside.

Mash the cooked pumpkin flesh until smooth with a potato masher or fork. Stir in the milk, bring to the boil and season to taste. Simmer for 6 minutes, adding more water if needed.

To serve, pour the soup into warmed bowls and top with the toasted bread chunks and pumpkin seeds.

MARROW, PEA & PAPRIKA SOUP

SERVES 4

1 medium marrow
1 tablespoon sunflower oil
1 medium onion, sliced
Freshly ground black pepper
1 oz (25 g) plain flour
1 pint (600 ml) semi-skimmed milk
10 fl oz (300 ml) vegetable stock
4 oz (100 g) frozen peas
Paprika to garnish

● Marrow has quite a delicate flavour and a lovely texture. You can adapt this recipe to use pumpkin instead of marrow if you wish.

Using a sharp knife, peel the marrow and cut in half lengthways. Scrape out the seeds with a spoon and discard them; cut the flesh into pieces. Heat the oil in a saucepan, add the marrow, onion and pepper. Cover and cook gently for 20 minutes, adding a little water if the pan goes dry.

Remove the saucepan from the heat and mash the cooked marrow until very smooth. Stir in the flour and gradually add the milk and stock. Stir well and return to the heat. Bring to the boil and simmer, uncovered, for a further 15 minutes.

If the soup is not smooth enough for your liking, process it in a liquidiser, then return it to the saucepan. Add the frozen peas and simmer for a final 5 minutes. Taste and adjust the seasoning if necessary. Pour into warm soup bowls and sprinkle with paprika.

SAVOY CABBAGE & ONION SOUP WITH MUSTARD BREAD

SERVES 4

1 tablespoon sunflower oil
1 lb (450 g) onions, finely sliced
1 lb (450 g) Savoy cabbage, finely chopped
1 bay leaf
1 oz (25 g) flour
1 clove garlic, crushed
2 pints (1.2 litres) vegetable stock
Freshly ground black pepper
2 tablespoons chopped parsley

FOR THE MUSTARD BREAD:

4 slices wholemeal French or other crusty wholemeal bread, crusts removed
2 oz (50 g) Cheddar cheese, grated
2 tablespoons French mustard

● This is one of my favourite winter soups. You can use any cabbage for this soup, but it is nicest made with a Savoy.

Heat the oil in a saucepan and add the onions, the cabbage and a splash of water. Cover with a tight-fitting lid, reduce the heat and cook the vegetables gently in their own juices for 15 minutes or until they are really soft.

Add the bay leaf, flour and garlic and stir well. Pour in the stock and season with black pepper. Stir thoroughly, bring to the boil and simmer for 25 minutes.

Meanwhile, make the mustard bread. Heat the grill and toast the bread on both sides. In a small bowl mix together the mustard and grated cheese. Spread the mixture on the toast, then return to the grill until the cheese has melted. Cut the mustard bread into large cubes.

Remove the soup from the heat, stir in the chopped parsley and taste to check the seasoning, adjusting it if necessary. Pour into warmed soup bowls and float the cubes of mustard bread on top.

CHUNKY CHICKEN & APPLE BROTH

SERVES 4

3 chicken legs, skin removed
2 medium leeks, sliced into thin rounds
1 lb (450 g) carrots, peeled and grated
4 oz (100 g) white cabbage, shredded
1 large potato, peeled and finely diced
1 clove garlic, crushed
2 pints (1.2 litres) vegetable stock
1 teaspoon dried thyme
Freshly ground black pepper
2 oz (50 g) porridge or jumbo oats
3 dessert apples, cored and sliced
2 tablespoons chopped parsley

● Apples and chicken are a great combination, but pears can make a good alternative for this chicken broth. Serve with warm oatcakes or granary toast.

In a large saucepan place the chicken legs, all the vegetables, the garlic, stock, thyme and black pepper. Bring to the boil, cover and simmer for 40 minutes.

Lift the chicken legs from the saucepan and remove the flesh from the bones. Discard the bones and return the flesh to the broth. Add the oats and apple slices and stir well. Simmer for a further 10 minutes, uncovered, adding extra vegetable stock or water if needed.

Taste the broth and adjust the seasoning if necessary. Stir in the parsley and serve piping hot.

MAIN COURSES

TIPS

- Use meat as a flavouring rather than as the main ingredient.

- When a recipe requires Cheddar cheese, substitute a low-fat type or Edam. However, by using a very mature Cheddar you will actually need less as it will give a very strong flavour.

- When frying, use oil sparingly: add just enough to grease the pan lightly.

- Instead of using fat, you can soften onions or vegetables by cooking them in a covered pan with a little water over a moderate heat for 3 minutes.

- To achieve the best result when using spices, always lightly fry first, stirring continuously for 1–2 minutes. However, take care not to burn them or a bitter taste will result.

- Seasoning is very important; a dish won't necessarily taste good just because it looks good, so always taste to check.

- When using meat, always trim away any obvious fat.

- You don't always need to peel vegetables: a good wash and scrub can sometimes be enough, especially in the case of potatoes and carrots.

- When using fish, use fresh whenever possible as frozen fish tends to lack flavour and texture.

● Always cook vegetables until just tender, otherwise they lose their flavour and texture.

● When using frozen meat, make sure that it is completely thawed before you start to cook.

● To test if chicken, turkey or pork is cooked, pierce close to the bone with a skewer or fork and check that the juices run clear with no trace of pink.

● Fruit goes well with meat, especially dried prunes and apricots, which happen to be full of fibre.

● When frying garlic, take care not to burn it as it will then taste bitter; it is better to discard burnt garlic and start again rather than persevere and spoil the dish.

CHINESE BEEF NOODLES

SERVES 4

8 oz (225 g) dried Chinese egg noodles
4 tablespoons soy sauce
2 teaspoons chilli sauce
1 tablespoon oyster sauce
2 tablespoons tomato purée
10 fl oz (300 ml) vegetable stock
1 teaspoon ground ginger
1 tablespoon sunflower oil
1 small green chilli pepper, de-seeded and finely chopped
1 clove garlic, crushed
8 oz (225 g) lean minced beef
1 green pepper, de-seeded and sliced
2 sticks celery, chopped
8 oz (225 g) carrots, peeled and cut into matchsticks
Freshly ground black pepper
4 oz (100 g) fresh spinach, stems removed, washed and shredded

- This recipe is a stir-fry, so have all the ingredients ready and prepared before you start cooking.

Plunge the Chinese noodles into boiling water and cook for 2 minutes. Drain and refresh under cold running water, and leave in a colander to drain. In a bowl mix together the soy sauce, chilli sauce, oyster sauce, tomato purée, stock and ginger.

Heat the oil in a large frying-pan or wok. Add the chilli pepper and garlic and cook for 10 seconds. Add the minced beef and stir-fry for 3 minutes. Add the green pepper, celery and carrots and stir-fry for a further 2 minutes. Lower the heat and pour in the stock mixture, taking care as it will splutter. Simmer for 5 minutes.

Add the drained noodles to the pan, toss and stir them for 1 minute to heat thoroughly. Season to taste. Just before serving, quickly stir in the shredded spinach and toss well. Pile into a warmed serving dish and serve at once.

BEEF & MUSHROOM LOAF WITH OLD-FASHIONED RED CABBAGE

SERVES 4

FOR THE LOAF:
8 oz (225 g) lean minced beef
2 cloves garlic, crushed
8 oz (225 g) carrots, grated
8 oz (225 g) large flat mushrooms, peeled and finely chopped
2 eggs
1 heaped tablespoon chopped fresh or 2 teaspoons dried oregano
1 medium onion, grated
2 oz (50 g) wholemeal breadcrumbs
Grated nutmeg to taste
2 tablespoons Worcestershire sauce
Freshly ground black pepper

FOR THE RED CABBAGE:
1¼ lb (500 g) red cabbage, shredded
2 large pears, peeled, cored and sliced
4 juniper berries, crushed (optional)
Pinch brown sugar
3 tablespoons wine vinegar
10 fl oz (300 ml) vegetable stock or water
Freshly ground black pepper
Watercress to garnish

• Red cabbage is a totally underrated vegetable which has a great flavour. Make sure that you shred it finely – it cooks better and looks more attractive. You will need a 1 lb (450 g) non-stick loaf tin for this recipe.

Pre-heat the oven to gas mark 5, 375°F, (190°C).

Mix the loaf ingredients together thoroughly and season well. Press into a 1 lb (450 g) non-stick loaf tin and cover with aluminium foil. Cook in the oven for 1¼ hours or until firm and a skewer or a knife comes out clean when inserted into the centre.

Meanwhile, mix together all the red cabbage ingredients, pack into a large casserole dish and cover with moistened greaseproof paper and a lid. Bake in the oven alongside the meat loaf for 1¼ hours or until the cabbage is tender.

When both loaf and cabbage are cooked, remove from the oven. Pour off and discard any excess liquid or fat in the loaf tin and turn out the loaf on to a large warmed platter. Surround with the hot red cabbage, or serve this separately in a dish. Garnish the meat loaf with the watercress.

HAM & LEEK GOUGÈRE

SERVES 4

FOR THE GOUGÈRE

10 fl oz (300 ml) cold water
2 oz (50 g) vegetable margarine
6 oz (175 g) wholemeal flour
3 small eggs, beaten

FOR THE FILLING:

8 medium leeks, trimmed
1 tablespoon sunflower oil
1 tablespoon chopped fresh or 1 teaspoon dried rosemary
6 slices lean ham, chopped
1 tablespoon plain flour
10 fl oz (300 ml) semi-skimmed milk
3 oz (75 g) Edam cheese, grated
1 tablespoon French or wholegrain mustard
Freshly ground black pepper
1 tablespoon wholemeal breadcrumbs

● Gougère is made with choux pastry, and makes a stunning, filling lunch or supper dish.

Pre-heat the oven to gas mark 6, 400°F (200°C).

First prepare the gougère. In a saucepan bring the water and margarine to a rapid boil. Lower the heat, add the flour and beat really well until the mixture leaves the sides of the pan. Remove from the heat and allow to cool for 5 minutes, then gradually add enough beaten egg to make a smooth, thick mixture (you may not need all the egg). Spoon the gougère around the edge of an ovenproof dish and set to one side.

Split the leeks in half lengthways and wash them well. Cook them in boiling water for 4 minutes or until just tender. Leave to drain in a colander.

Heat the oil in a saucepan, add the rosemary and ham cook for 1 minute. Remove the pan from the heat and stir in the flour. Pour in the milk and whisk until smooth. Return the pan to the heat and bring to the boil, stirring continuously, until thick. Reduce the heat and simmer the sauce for a further 4 minutes. Add the cheese and mustard and mix until smooth. Season to taste.

Place the drained leeks in the centre of the ovenproof dish, pour over the cheese and ham sauce and sprinkle with breadcrumbs. Bake in the oven for 35–40 minutes or until the gougère is risen, crisp and golden-brown. Serve at once.

PASTA BOWS
WITH CAULIFLOWER & BACON

SERVES 4

1 tablespoon sunflower oil
1 onion, finely chopped
1 medium cauliflower, broken into florets
10 coriander seeds, crushed
5 tomatoes, chopped
1 teaspoon dried basil
Freshly ground black pepper
5 fl oz (150 ml) vegetable stock
4 rashers rindless bacon
14 oz (400 g) wholemeal pasta bows
3 courgettes, grated
2 oz (50 g) Edam cheese, grated

• A filling, tasty pasta dish. Grind over plenty of black pepper and serve with a crisp green salad.

Heat the oil in a saucepan and add the onion, cauliflower florets, coriander seeds, tomatoes, basil and pepper. Cover and cook gently for 3 minutes. Add the stock, cover again and simmer for a further 15–20 minutes or until the cauliflower is tender.

Meanwhile, grill the bacon until crisp and chop. Cook the pasta in boiling salted water until just tender but still slightly firm, then drain.

Add the pasta to the cauliflower mixture and stir in the grated courgettes. Season to taste. Pile into a warmed serving dish and scatter over the chopped bacon and grated cheese. Serve at once.

HUNGARIAN PORK

SERVES 4

12 oz (350 g) lean shoulder of pork, diced
2 tablespoons paprika
Freshly ground black pepper
2 large onions, finely sliced
1 × 14 oz (400 g) tin chopped tomatoes
2 tablespoons tomato purée
1 pint (600 ml) vegetable stock
1½ lb (750 g) unpeeled potatoes, washed and diced
4 oz (100 g) button mushrooms, halved

FOR THE GARNISH:
5 fl oz (150 ml) natural yoghurt
Grated rind 1 lemon
2 tablespoons chopped parsley

• When you are on the road, look out for a good hearty meal like this one. At home serve it with jacket potatoes and stir-fried cabbage.

Toss the diced pork in the paprika and grind over plenty of black pepper. Put the onions in a large saucepan and add 3 tablespoons cold water, cover with a tight-fitting lid and cook gently for 5 minutes. Remove the lid, increase the heat and cook the onions more briskly, stirring continuously, for 2 minutes. Lower the heat again, add the pork and cook lightly for 3 minutes. Stir in the tomatoes, tomato purée and stock. Season, cover and simmer gently for 40 mins.

Add the potatoes to the saucepan and cook for a further 35–40 minutes, adding extra stock or water if needed. Put in the mushrooms 15 minutes before the end of the cooking time. Season to taste and ladle into a warmed casserole or serving dish. Drizzle over the natural yoghurt and sprinkle with lemon rind and parsley.

LAMB
& BUTTERBEAN CASSEROLE

SERVES 4

10 oz (275 g) butterbeans, soaked overnight in cold water
1 tablespoon sunflower oil
12 oz (350 g) lean lamb, cubed
2 cloves garlic
2 sticks celery, chopped
1 onion, chopped
1 × 14 oz (400 g) tin tomatoes
1 pint (600 ml) vegetable stock or water
5 fl oz (150 ml) beer
2 teaspoons dill seed (optional)
1 bay leaf
Freshly ground black pepper
Chopped parsley to garnish

• Serve this deliciously thick casserole with warm hunks of granary bread and plenty of steamed vegetables.

Pre-heat the oven to gas mark 3, 325°F (160°C).

Drain the beans, put them in a saucepan and cover with fresh cold water. Bring to the boil, boil rapidly for 10 minutes, then drain.

Heat the oil in a frying-pan, add the lamb and fry quickly until lightly browned on all sides. With a slotted spoon transfer the meat to an ovenproof dish or casserole. Reduce the heat under the frying-pan and add the garlic, celery and onion. Fry gently until for about 5 minutes or until lightly browned. Add the beans and remaining ingredients (except the parsley) and bring to the boil. Season well and pour over the lamb. Cover and bake in the oven for 2½ hours or until the beans are cooked and soft and the meat is falling apart. Add more stock or water if needed.

Serve scattered with plenty of chopped parsley.

CHICKEN & APPLE CRUMBLE

SERVES 4

2 lb (1 kg) cooked chicken
8 oz (225 g) broccoli florets
1 tablespoon sunflower oil
1 onion, chopped
2 dessert apples, cored and chopped
1 tablespoon plain flour
1 teaspoon ground turmeric
10 fl oz (300 ml) semi-skimmed milk
½ vegetable stock cube
Freshly ground black pepper

FOR THE TOPPING:
2 oz (50 g) jumbo or porridge oats
2 oz (50 g) wholemeal breadcrumbs
1 tablespoon sunflower oil
2 tablespoons chopped parsley

● This unusual crumble is warming and very tasty. Serve it with a salad or vegetables.

Pre-heat the oven to gas mark 5, 375°F (190°C).

Remove the skin and bones from the chicken and discard. Cut the chicken flesh into 2 inch (5 cm) pieces and place in an ovenproof dish.

Cook the broccoli florets in a pan of boiling salted water for 2–3 minutes or until just tender. Drain and refresh under cold running water, drain again and add to the chicken.

In a saucepan heat the oil, add the onion and fry for 2 minutes. Stir in the apples and cook for 1 minute. Remove the pan from the heat, add the flour and turmeric and stir well. Pour in all the milk and continue stirring until smooth. Return the pan to the heat and bring slowly to the boil, stirring all the time. Add the ½ stock cube and simmer the sauce for 3 minutes. Season with black pepper. Add extra milk if the sauce is too thick. Pour over the chicken and broccoli.

Mix together the oats, breadcrumbs, oil and parsley. Sprinkle this over the chicken and bake for 30–35 minutes or until golden on top and bubbling hot.

CHICKEN SALAD PANCAKES

SERVES 4

FOR THE BATTER:
2 oz (50 g) wholemeal flour
4 teaspoons curry powder
1 teaspoon ground coriander
1 egg
5 fl oz (150 ml) semi-skimmed milk
Freshly ground black pepper

FOR THE CHICKEN SALAD:
3 oz (75 g) button mushrooms, sliced
Juice ½ lemon
10 fl oz (300 ml) fromage frais
1 tablespoon horseradish sauce
8 oz (225 g) cooked chicken, cut into bite-sized pieces
4 tomatoes, finely chopped
1 banana, peeled and sliced
Freshly ground black pepper
1 punnet mustard and cress to garnish

● Chicken and horseradish blend particularly well in these spicy pancakes. Serve with a crisp green salad or freshly cooked vegetables.

Make the batter by simply mixing all the ingredients together. Set aside.

Sprinkle the sliced mushrooms with lemon juice and allow to stand for 5 minutes. Then put them in a large bowl with the fromage frais, horseradish sauce, chicken, tomatoes and banana. Stir gently to combine and season to taste.

With the batter make 4 pancakes and set them aside to cool.

Fill the cooled pancakes with the chicken salad and roll up into fat cigars. Alternatively, fold the pancakes in half and then in half again so that they form cornets which can be opened and filled. Arrange the filled pancakes attractively on a large serving dish and scatter over the mustard and cress.

PEASANT CHICKEN

SERVES 4

1 × 3 lb (1.5 kg) chicken
2 cloves garlic, crushed (optional)
2 medium leeks, cut in half
4 small onions, peeled and studded with cloves
4 small parsnips, peeled
4 small turnips, peeled
1 lb (450 g) medium unpeeled potatoes, washed and cut in half
1 small Savoy cabbage, cut into quarters
Freshly ground black pepper
6 cardamom pods, crushed
6 black peppercorns
1 bay leaf
12 oz (350 g) broken spaghetti or vermicelli
3 tablespoons chopped fresh herbs

● This is a real winter warmer, a soupy stew full of vegetables, chicken, herbs and pasta: delicious! Serve with warm granary bread.

Wash the chicken inside and out and place in a large pan with the prepared vegetables. Cover with cold water and add all the remaining ingredients except the pasta and the chopped fresh herbs. Put the lid on the pan and bring to the boil, then simmer for 1¼–1½ hours or until the chicken is cooked and the vegetables are tender.

Using 2 large slotted spoons, remove the chicken from the pan and place on a large platter. Remove the vegetables in the same way. Using two forks, remove the flesh from the chicken and discard the bones and skin.

Using a ladle or large spoon, remove any scum and or fat from the broth in which the chicken was cooked. Bring the broth back to the boil, add the broken spaghetti or vermicelli and simmer for a few minutes or until the pasta is cooked. Season the broth to taste.

Meanwhile, divide the vegetables and chicken flesh between 4 large soup bowls. Ladle over the hot spaghetti broth and scatter with chopped herbs.

MUSTARD CHICKEN
& BEAN FLAN WITH CHILLI SAUCE

SERVES 4

FOR THE WHOLEMEAL SHORTCRUST PASTRY:
6 oz (175 g) wholemeal flour
Pinch salt
3 oz (75 g) vegetable margarine
4–5 tablespoons cold water

FOR THE FILLING:
5 oz (150 g) black-eye beans
5 oz (150 g) cooked chicken flesh, chopped
2 eggs, beaten
5 fl oz (150 ml) natural yoghurt
2 tablespoons semi-skimmed milk
1 teaspoon wholemeal flour
Freshly ground black pepper
1 teaspoon paprika
2 tablespoons French or wholegrain mustard
Chopped parsley to garnish

FOR THE CHILLI SAUCE:
5 fl oz (150 ml) tomato juice
1 clove garlic, crushed (optional)
Tabasco sauce to taste
Freshly ground black pepper

● The mustard base gives this flan a really zingy flavour. Use French or wholegrain mustard as English mustard is far too strong. The flan is best served hot or warm with a crisp green salad or steamed vegetables.

Put the beans for the filling in a saucepan, cover with cold water and bring to the boil. Boil rapidly for 10 minutes, then put the lid on the pan and simmer for 35–40 minutes or until tender. Drain well.

Now make the pastry. Sift the flour and salt together. Rub in the margarine with your fingertips until the mixture resembles breadcrumbs.

Sprinkle over the water and mix together quickly to form a soft but not sticky dough. Form into a ball.

Pre-heat the oven to gas mark 6, 400°F (200°C). Roll out the pastry on a floured board or work-surface and use it to line an 8 inch (20 cm) flan tin. Prick the base well with a fork and chill in the refrigerator for 15 minutes (this prevents shrinkage).

Meanwhile, prepare the chilli sauce by mixing all the ingredients together. Season to taste.

In a large bowl combine all the filling ingredients except the mustard and parsley. Taste and adjust the seasoning if necessary. Remove the flan case from the refrigerator and spread the base with mustard. Spoon in the filling and bake in the oven for 30–35 minutes or until set.

Trickle the chilli sauce, hot or cold, in a whirl on top of the flan, or hand it separately in a sauce boat. Scatter the flan with plenty of chopped parsley before serving.

CHICKEN & VEGETABLE ROAST WITH RED PEPPER GRAVY

SERVES 4

1 tablespoon sunflower oil
1 medium onion, chopped
1 clove garlic, crushed
8 oz (225 g) courgettes, grated
2 large carrots, peeled and grated
Freshly ground black pepper
1 lb (450 g) uncooked boneless chicken, minced
5 fl oz (150 ml) tomato juice
2 tablespoons tomato purée
1 tablespoon Worcestershire sauce
4 oz (100 g) porridge oats
2 tablespoons chopped parsley
1 egg, beaten
4 oz (100 g) runner beans
Watercress to garnish

FOR THE GRAVY:

1 medium onion, chopped
1 large red pepper, de-seeded and chopped
1 teaspoon dried thyme
1 × 14 oz (400 g) tin chopped tomatoes
1 tablespoon tomato purée
1 clove garlic, crushed
Freshly ground black pepper

• Serve this chicken roast cold with a crisp green salad instead of with its red pepper gravy if you wish. You will need a 2 lb (1 kg) loaf or cake tin.

Pre-heat the oven to gas mark 5, 375°F (190°C). Lightly grease a 2 lb (1 kg) loaf or cake tin.

Heat the oil in a frying-pan, put in the onion, garlic, courgettes and carrots, sprinkle with black pepper and fry over a medium heat for 5 minutes, stirring constantly. Remove the pan from the heat and tip the mixture into a large mixing bowl. Return the pan to the heat and add the chicken. Toss and stir for 4 minutes, then stir in the tomato juice and purée and mix well. Tip this mixture into the bowl of vegetables. Add the Worcestershire sauce, oats, parsley and egg. Stir the mixture well and season to taste.

Cook the beans in boiling water for 2 minutes, then drain and refresh under cold running water. Drain again thoroughly.

Put half the chicken mixture into the prepared tin and arrange a layer of beans on top. Cover with the remaining mixture, press down well and cover with aluminium foil. Place the tin in a roasting tin half-full of boiling water and bake in the oven for 1¼ hours.

Meanwhile, make the gravy by gently simmering all the ingredients together in a covered saucepan for 25 minutes. Liquidise until smooth and return to the saucepan to re-heat gently. Add a little water to the gravy if it is too thick. Taste and adjust the seasoning if necessary.

Remove the roast from the oven and allow to cool for 10 minutes in the tin. Pour off any excess liquid, run a knife around the edge of the roast and turn out carefully on to a warmed serving dish. Serve whole or cut into thick slices. Decorate with a large bunch of watercress and hand the hot sauce separately.

CHICKEN & DILL PAELLA

SERVES 4

6 chicken drumsticks
2 teaspoons ground turmeric
Freshly ground black pepper
1 tablespoon sunflower oil
1 leek, sliced
1 stick celery, chopped
1 green pepper, de-seeded and sliced
1 clove garlic, crushed
10 oz (275 g) brown rice
2 oz (50 g) raisins
1 bay leaf
1 1/2 pints (900 ml) vegetable stock or water
1 level teaspoon dill seeds
6 oz (175 g) frozen peas

FOR THE GARNISH:
3 tomatoes, finely chopped
2 tablespoons chopped parsley
2 tablespoons natural yoghurt

• Paella traditionally includes shellfish, but you can make a much simpler version, as in this recipe.

Skin the chicken legs, toss in the turmeric and grind over some black pepper. Heat the oil in a large, lidded frying-pan or wok, add the chicken legs and toss over a high heat for 2 minutes. Remove the chicken from the pan with a slotted spoon and set to one side. Add the leek, celery, green pepper and garlic to the oil remaining in the pan and cook for 2 minutes. Stir in the rice, raisins and bay leaf and return the chicken legs to the pan. Pour in the vegetable stock or water, add the dill seeds, cover and cook for 35–40 minutes, adding more stock or water if necessary. Season to taste.

The paella is ready when the rice is just tender and the liquid has been absorbed. When it has reached this stage, remove the lid and gently stir in the peas. Remove from the heat, cover again and leave to stand for 5 minutes.

To serve, take the lid off the pan, sprinkle over the chopped tomatoes and parsley and top with a whirl of yoghurt.

TURKEY, ORANGE & THYME PARCELS

SERVES 4

4 turkey escalopes

FOR THE MARINADE:
½ bunch spring onions, chopped
2 teaspoons dried thyme
6 tablespoons light soy sauce
1 clove garlic, crushed
Grated rind and juice 1 large orange
1 tablespoon sunflower oil
Freshly ground black pepper

● The combination of orange and thyme goes well with turkey. Serve with brown rice and plenty of steamed peppered vegetables.

Pre-heat the oven to gas mark 5, 375°C (190°C).

In a large bowl mix together the marinade ingredients. Trim any fat from the turkey escalopes, place them in the marinade and leave to stand for 30 minutes.

Cut 4 large squares of aluminium foil and place a turkey escalope on each piece. Spoon over the marinade and seal each piece of foil to form a parcel. Place the parcels on a baking sheet and bake in the oven for 20–25 minutes. Serve the turkey in the foil parcels – the diners open these themselves to enjoy the wonderful aroma that is released.

TURKEY & CHESTNUT PIE

SERVES 4

8 oz (225 g) Wholemeal Shortcrust Pastry (see page 63)
1 tablespoon sunflower oil
1 onion, finely chopped
8 oz (225 g) carrots, grated
1 oz (25 g) plain flour
10 fl oz (300 ml) vegetable stock
Juice 1 large orange
12 oz (350 g) cooked turkey, chopped
4 oz (100 g) cooked runner beans
8 oz (225 g) chestnuts, peeled and chopped
Freshly ground black pepper
Milk for glazing

● The traditional way of dealing with chestnuts is to roast them in the ashes of a fire. However, if you are using them in a savoury dish, just make a slit in the brown skin and plunge them into boiling water for 4 minutes, then drain and peel quickly before the skins cool and harden.

First make the pastry. Wrap it in cling film and leave to rest in the refrigerator.

Meanwhile, heat the oil in a saucepan, add the onion and carrots, cover with a lid and cook gently for 3 minutes. Add the flour and mix well. Remove from the heat, pour in the stock and orange juice and stir until smooth. Return to the heat, bring to the boil, stirring constantly until thick, and simmer for 4 minutes, adding extra stock or water if necessary. Remove from the heat and leave to cool.

Pre-heat the oven to gas mark 6, 400°F (200°C).

Stir the turkey, runner beans and chestnuts into the cooled sauce, season to taste and pour into a pie-dish. On a floured board or work-surface, roll out the pastry and use to cover the pie. Trim the edges neatly and pinch with your fingers to decorate. Roll out the pastry trimmings and cut into thin strips. Arrange in a lattice pattern over the pie lid. Brush with milk and bake in the oven for 35 minutes or until golden.

BAKED FISH POTATOES WITH SPINACH & SUNFLOWER SALAD

SERVES 4

8 oz (225 g) cod, whiting or haddock fillet
2 large potatoes, baked in their skins
3 tablespoons natural yoghurt
1 large carrot, grated
½ bunch spring onions, chopped
Freshly ground black pepper
1 oz (25 g) Cheddar cheese, grated
1 tablespoon wholemeal breadcrumbs

FOR THE SALAD:
4 oz (100 g) fresh spinach
Juice ½ lemon
2 tablespoons sunflower oil
1 oz (25 g) sunflower seeds

● The secret of retaining the flavour, texture and appearance of fresh spinach is either to cook it quickly by stir-frying or to eat it raw as a salad ingredient – as in this recipe, to accompany the tasty fish potatoes.

Pre-heat the oven to gas mark 6, 400°F (200°C).

Place the fish fillet in a saucepan and barely cover with water. Simmer for 6 minutes or until just cooked. Remove with a fish slice and leave the fish to cool on a plate, then peel off the skin and flake the flesh.

Cut the baked potatoes in half and scoop out the flesh into a mixing bowl. Add the yoghurt, carrot, spring onions and flaked fish. Mash well and season to taste. Spoon the mixture into the potato skins, sprinkle with the cheese and breadcrumbs and bake in the oven for 15–20 minutes or until the topping is golden brown.

Meanwhile prepare the salad. Remove the stems from the spinach leaves and discard. Tear the leaves into pieces and wash thoroughly. Drain and dry well. Toss the spinach with the lemon juice, sunflower oil and seeds and season with black pepper. Serve with the fish potatoes.

TUSCANY PASTA

SERVES 4

1 tablespoon sunflower oil
1 tablespoon chopped fresh thyme
1 × 9 oz (250 g) tin red kidney beans, drained
5 fl oz (150 ml) vegetable stock
Freshly ground black pepper
10 oz (275 g) wholemeal pasta twists
2 × 4 oz (100 g) tins smoked mussels, drained

FOR THE CHILLI SAUCE:
10 fl oz (300 ml) tomato juice
Pinch brown sugar
Freshly ground black pepper
2 cloves garlic, crushed
About 1 teaspoon Tabasco sauce, or to taste

- The smoked mussels give this dish a wonderful flavour. They're not expensive and you will find them in most major supermarkets. Tinned tuna or sardines make a good alternative.

Heat the oil in a saucepan, add the thyme, kidney beans and stock. Season with black pepper, cover and cook for 15 minutes.

Meanwhile, combine the sauce ingredients and heat in a saucepan. Season to taste. In another pan cook the pasta in boiling water until tender but still firm to the bite, then drain.

Add the pasta to the beans, stir and cook for 2 minutes. Pile into a large warmed serving bowl. Scatter over the drained smoked mussels and serve at once, handing the hot chilli sauce separately.

FISH IN OATMEAL WITH HOT CUCUMBER

SERVES 4

5 oz (150 g) porridge oats
Freshly ground black pepper
4 herrings or *small mackerel, filleted*
1/2 cucumber
2 tablespoons sunflower oil
2 teaspoons dried thyme
Juice 1 lemon
6 radishes, sliced, and 1 tablespoon chopped parsley to garnish

• For this dish the fish is baked in oatmeal and thyme and served with hot cucumber.

Pre-heat the oven to gas mark 5, 375°F (190°C).

Put the porridge oats in a roasting tin and season with black pepper. Coat the fish fillets with the oats by pressing each side into them.

Cut the cucumber in half lengthways, remove the channel of seeds with a teaspoon and discard them. Slice the cucumber into crescents.

Heat the oil in a large frying-pan, lay the fish fillets in it, skin side up, and cook for 1 minute. Using a fish slice carefully turn over the fillets and cook for a further minute. Transfer the fish to an ovenproof dish, sprinkle over the thyme and lemon juice and cover with aluminium foil. Bake in the oven for 10–15 minutes or until the fish is just cooked.

Meanwhile, cook the cucumber in boiling water for 1 minute, drain and season with black pepper.

To serve, scatter the baked fish with hot cucumber and sprinkle over the radishes and parsley.

CRACKED WHEAT
FISH CRUMBLE

SERVES 4

2 oz (50 g) red lentils
2 oz (50 g) cracked wheat
1 lb (450 g) cod, hake or haddock fillets, skinned
Juice 1 lemon
3 tablespoons sunflower oil
1 medium onion, chopped
1 clove garlic, crushed
1 tablespoon chopped mint
1 × 14 oz (400 g) tin tomatoes
1 tablespoon tomato purée
Pinch brown sugar
Freshly ground black pepper
2 tablespoons low-fat cream or curd cheese
2 oz (50 g) wholemeal flour
2 oz (50 g) porridge oats
2 tablespoons chopped fresh herbs to garnish

• The combination of porridge oats and cracked wheat makes a delightful crunchy topping to this savoury fish crumble.

Pre-heat the oven to gas mark 6, 400°F (200°C).

Place the lentils in a saucepan, cover with cold water and simmer for 15 minutes or until soft. Drain off any water not absorbed during cooking. Put the cracked wheat in a bowl, cover with cold water and leave to soak for 15 minutes, then drain well. Cut the fish into 2 inch (5 cm) pieces and place in an ovenproof dish. Scatter over the lentils and lemon juice.

In a saucepan heat 1 tablespoon of the oil, add the onion and garlic and cook over a medium heat for 3 minutes. Add the mint, tomatoes, tomato purée, sugar and pepper and simmer for 15 minutes. Season to taste, whisk in the cream or curd cheese and pour the sauce over the fish and lentils.

In a large bowl mix the drained, cracked wheat with the wholemeal flour, porridge oats and remaining 2 tablespoons oil. Sprinkle the mixture over the fish and lentils and bake in the oven for 25–30 minutes or until bubbling hot and golden on top. Scatter with the chopped fresh herbs and serve.

CHOWDER BAKE

SERVES 4

8 oz (225 g) broccoli florets
1 bunch spring onions, chopped
1 × 7 oz (200 g) tin tuna in brine, drained
3 tomatoes, chopped
1 × 10½ oz (298 g) tin creamed sweetcorn
1 × 7 oz (200 g) tin sweetcorn, drained
Freshly ground black pepper
4 slices granary bread
1 oz (25 g) Edam cheese, grated

- A real store-cupboard treat. Cauliflower can be used in place of the broccoli if you prefer.

Pre-heat the oven to gas mark 6, 400°F (200°C).

Cook the broccoli florets in boiling water until just tender. Drain and refresh under cold running water.

In a large bowl combine half the spring onions with the tuna, tomatoes, broccoli and sweetcorn and season to taste. Pile into a shallow ovenproof dish.

Toast the bread, cut into triangles and arrange round the edge of the dish. Sprinkle over the cheese and remaining spring onions. Bake in the oven for 15–20 minutes or until bubbling hot. Serve at once.

KEDGEREE PIE

SERVES 4

FOR THE PASTRY:

4 oz (100 g) vegetable margarine
1 teaspoon curry powder
About 5 tablespoons cold water
8 oz (225 g) wholemeal flour
A little milk

FOR THE FILLING:

5 oz (150 g) brown rice, cooked and drained
1 teaspoon curry powder
3 × 4½ oz (120 g) tins sardines in tomato sauce, mashed
1 egg, beaten
2 large carrots, washed and grated
2 tomatoes, chopped
1 bunch spring onions, chopped
Freshly ground black pepper

● Serve this tasty pie with a crisp green salad. Tuna fish can be used instead of sardines if you wish.

First make the pastry. In a saucepan melt the margarine with the curry powder. Remove from the heat and allow to cool, then stir in the water. Pour the cold liquid over the flour and mix together to form a soft but not sticky dough. Knead on a board or work-surface until firm, wrap in cling film and chill in the refrigerator for 15 minutes.

Pre-heat the oven to gas mark 6, 400°F (200°C). Combine all the filling ingredients in a bowl and season well.

Roll out the pastry to a 12 inch (30 cm) square. Place on a floured baking sheet and spoon on the filling, leaving the corners of the pastry clear. Brush the edges of the pastry with water, draw the two front corners up and pinch together. Repeat with the remaining corners. Brush all over with milk and bake in the oven for 25–30 minutes or until crisp and golden. Serve hot or cold.

HAZELNUT BUBBLE & SQUEAK

SERVES 4

8 oz (225 g) cooked greens, cabbage or *kale*
2 lb (1 kg) cooked mashed potatoes
2 carrots, grated
1 onion, sliced
Pinch ground nutmeg
½ teaspoon yeast extract
Freshly ground black pepper
1 tablespoon sunflower oil
1 oz (25 g) hazelnuts, chopped
1 tablespoon wholemeal breadcrumbs
1 oz (25 g) strong Cheddar cheese, grated

● I adore bubble and squeak – it is a perfect way of using left-over vegetables. Serve it as a main meal with plenty of freshly ground black pepper and a large tossed salad.

Finely shred or chop the cooked greens, cabbage or kale. In a large bowl mix them with the mashed potatoes.

Place the carrots, onion, nutmeg, yeast extract and a splash of water in a saucepan. Cover and cook over a gentle heat for 4 minutes (the vegetables will cook in their own juices). Stir the contents of the pan into the potato mixture, combine thoroughly and season to taste.

Heat the oil in a frying-pan. When the oil is very hot, spread the mixture evenly in the pan. Cook over a medium heat until the underside is crisp and golden.

Towards the end of the frying time, pre-heat the grill. When the underside of the bubble and squeak is golden, place it under the grill and grill until the top is brown. Sprinkle over the hazelnuts, breadcrumbs and cheese and grill again until this topping is golden-brown.

Divide the bubble and squeak into 4 wedges and serve at once.

GREEN CHEESE LASAGNE

SERVES 4

1 lb (450 g) frozen spinach, thawed
8 oz (225 g) cooked cabbage or *greens, shredded*
1 clove garlic, crushed
1 teaspoon dried basil
Pinch ground nutmeg
Freshly ground black pepper
6 oz (175 g) curd cheese
5 tablespoons natural yoghurt
8 oz (225 g) green or wholemeal lasagne that does not need pre-cooking

FOR THE TOPPING:
10 fl oz (300 ml) natural yoghurt
1 egg
1 egg white
1 tablespoon grated Parmesan cheese
4 tomatoes, sliced
Ground nutmeg
Freshly ground black pepper
2 tablespoons wholemeal breadcrumbs

- To save time, use lasagne that requires no pre-cooking for this recipe – it is available at most supermarkets. If you wish you can add some chopped smoked bacon to this meatless lasagne.

Pre-heat the oven to gas mark 5, 375°C (190°C).

Finely chop the thawed spinach and place it in a saucepan. Cook for 3 minutes, stirring well to evaporate all the liquid. Add the chopped cabbage or greens, garlic, basil, nutmeg and pepper and fry for a further 2 minutes. Remove from the heat and stir in the curd cheese and 5 tablespoons yoghurt. Season to taste.

In a greased ovenproof dish, put a layer of the spinach mixture, then a layer of the lasagne. Repeat with a layer of spinach and then finish with a layer of lasagne.

Now prepare the topping. In a small bowl mix together the yoghurt with the egg, egg white and Parmesan. Spoon and spread over the lasagne. Arrange the tomato slices over the top. Sprinkle with plenty of nutmeg and black pepper and scatter over the breadcrumbs. Bake in the oven for 35–40 minutes or until bubbling hot and golden-brown.

PASTA TWISTS WITH PUMPKIN & GREEN BEANS

SERVES 4

12 oz (350 g) pumpkin
1 tablespoon sunflower oil
Pinch ground nutmeg
2 cloves garlic, crushed
3 tablespoons orange juice
7 oz (200 g) wholemeal pasta twists
7 oz (200 g) green or plain pasta twists
4 oz (100 g) fresh or frozen green beans, topped, tailed and cut in half
Freshly ground black pepper

- The essence of any pasta dish is not to overcook the pasta. It is better to undercook it, so that it stays firm to the bite and doesn't lose its texture.

Peel the pumpkin and cut the flesh into cubes, reserving the seeds. Wash and dry the seeds, place in a saucepan and fry without fat until roasted.

Heat the oil in a frying-pan, add the diced pumpkin, nutmeg and garlic and fry for 3 minutes. Reduce the heat and pour in the orange juice. Cook, stirring occasionally, for 10 minutes or until the pumpkin is tender but not mushy.

Meanwhile, cook the pasta in plenty of boiling water for 6–8 minutes or until just tender but still very firm to the bite. Add the beans to the pasta and cook for a further minute, then drain well. Stir the pasta and beans into the pumpkin and season to taste. Pile into a warmed serving dish and scatter with the roasted pumpkin seeds. Serve at once.

RATATOUILLE WITH CORN CAKES

SERVES 4

FOR THE RATATOUILLE:

1 tablespoon sunflower oil
1 medium onion, chopped
1 clove garlic, crushed
1 medium aubergine, cut into chunks
1 medium unpeeled potato, washed and chopped
3 courgettes, sliced
Freshly ground black pepper
4 tomatoes, roughly chopped
1 × 14 oz (400 g) tin tomatoes
1 teaspoon dried oregano
1 bay leaf
Paprika to garnish

FOR THE CORN CAKES:

1 × 7 oz (200 g) tin sweetcorn
1 egg
1½ oz (40 g) wholemeal flour
4 tablespoons milk
1 tablespoon sunflower oil, plus extra for greasing
Freshly ground black pepper

• Serve this ratatouille piping hot with a plateful of warm corn cakes. Diced cooked chicken or ham can be added to the ratatouille at the last moment, if desired.

Mix together the corn cake ingredients, cover and chill in the refrigerator for 20 minutes.

Meanwhile, prepare the ratatouille. Heat the oil in a large pan, add the onion, garlic and aubergine and fry for 4 minutes. Add the potato, courgettes and pepper. Cover and cook for a further 5 minutes. Add the remaining ingredients except the paprika and simmer, covered, for a further 15–20 minutes. Season to taste.

While the ratatouille is cooking, make the corn cakes. Lightly grease a frying-pan with a little sunflower oil and place over a high heat until hot. Add 2 tablespoons of the corn mixture to the pan and cook for about 1 minute on each side or until golden. The mixture will make 8–10 cakes.

Pour the ratatouille into a warmed serving dish, sprinkle generously with paprika and serve with the corn cakes.

EASY VEGETABLE CURRY WITH RAITA

SERVES 4

FOR THE CURRY:
1 medium cauliflower, broken into florets
8 oz (225 g) frozen peas
4 oz (100 g) fresh or frozen runner beans
1 lb (450 g) unpeeled potatoes, washed and cut into large cubes
1 tablespoon sunflower oil
4 tablespoons garam masala or good-quality curry powder
1 tablespoon tomato purée
1 oz (25 g) plain flour
1 pint (600 ml) vegetable stock or water
Freshly ground black pepper
4 oz (100 g) low-fat cream or curd cheese
Chopped mint to garnish

FOR THE RAITA:
5 fl oz (150 ml) natural yoghurt
1 teaspoon mint sauce
1/4 cucumber, cut into thin slices
1 tomato, chopped
Freshly ground black pepper
Paprika to garnish

● Warming, tasty and quick! Serve it with brown rice or noodles. It is important that you allow the curry spice to cook for 30 seconds in the oil as this will enhance the flavour of your vegetable curry.

Cook the cauliflower, peas and beans in boiling water for 2 minutes, then drain well. Boil the potatoes for 3–4 minutes in water and drain well.

In a saucepan heat the oil, stir in the garam masala or curry powder and cook for 30 seconds. Stir in the tomato purée and flour and mix thoroughly. Add the potatoes and stock, stir well, cover and simmer for 6 minutes. Add the remaining vegetables and season to taste. Cover and cook for a further 10 minutes or until the vegetables are tender. Add extra stock or water if the curry becomes dry.

Meanwhile, make the raita. Simply mix together all the ingredients apart from the paprika and season to taste. Spoon the raita into a serving dish and sprinkle with paprika.

Just before serving, stir the low-fat cheese into the curry, ladle into a warmed serving dish and scatter over the chopped mint. Serve with the raita.

LEMON & CORIANDER KEBABS

SERVES 4

FOR THE MARINADE:
Grated rind and juice of 1 lemon
1 clove garlic, crushed
2 tablespoons chopped parsley
1 tablespoon sunflower oil
10 coriander seeds, crushed
3 tablespoons soy sauce

FOR THE KEBABS:
8 small unpeeled potatoes or large potato chunks, washed
8 cauliflower florets
1 red pepper, de-seeded and cut in 8 pieces
1 green pepper, de-seeded and cut in 8 pieces
8 medium mushrooms
2 medium courgettes, each cut in 6 rounds

FOR THE SAUCE:

8 oz (225 g) red lentils, picked over
1 tablespoon sunflower oil
1 level teaspoon chilli powder
1 teaspoon ground coriander
Freshly ground black pepper
1¾ pints (1 litre) vegetable stock or water
3 tablespoons natural yoghurt

- Kebabs are delicious, but can seem a little meagre. However, in this recipe the vegetable kebabs are served with a lentil dhal, which makes a tasty, filling accompaniment. Brown rice will complete this satisfying main course.

First make the sauce. In a covered saucepan simmer the lentils, oil and spices in the vegetable stock or water for 1 hour or until the lentils are mushy and the sauce is of a thick consistency. Season to taste.

Meanwhile, cook the potatoes and cauliflower in boiling water until just tender. Drain well. In a large bowl mix together the marinade ingredients. Add the potatoes, cauliflower and the rest of the kebab vegetables and toss them in the marinade. Leave to stand for 1 hour.

When you are ready to cook the kebabs, pre-heat the grill to medium. Remove the vegetables from the marinade and skewer them alternately on to metal or wooden skewers. Place on a baking sheet, spoon the remaining marinade over the kebabs and cook under the grill for 7–10 minutes, turning occasionally, until sizzling and very hot.

Re-heat the lentil sauce, remove it from the heat and stir in the yoghurt. Pile into a warmed bowl and serve with the vegetable kebabs.

COURGETTE & NUT ROAST WITH CARROT CREAM

SERVES 4

FOR THE ROAST:
8 oz (225 g) hazelnuts and almonds, finely chopped
1 tablespoon sunflower oil
1 large onion, finely chopped
2 teaspoons dried marjoram
2 teaspoons yeast extract
2 eggs
1 green pepper, finely chopped
4 oz (100 g) wholemeal breadcrumbs
1 lb (450 g) courgettes, grated
Freshly ground black pepper
Watercress to garnish

FOR THE CARROT CREAM:
2 lb (1 kg) carrots, peeled and finely sliced
1 bay leaf
Freshly ground black pepper

● This courgette and nut roast makes a statisfying meal and is delicious served with the carrot cream and baked jacket potatoes.

Pre-heat the oven to gas mark 5, 375°F (190°C). Place the nuts on a baking sheet and bake in the oven until lightly browned.

Heat the oil in a frying-pan, add the onion and cook for 4 minutes. Add the marjoram and yeast extract and remove from the heat.

In a large bowl mix together the nuts, onion mixture and all the remaining roast ingredients except the watercress. Season to taste. Stir well and pack into a greased, shallow, oblong ovenproof dish. Bake in the oven for 35–40 minutes or until firm.

Meanwhile, make the carrot cream. Place the sliced carrots in a saucepan, cover with water and add the bay leaf and seasoning. Cover and cook over a moderate heat for about 20 minutes or until very, very tender, adding extra water if needed. Drain the carrots and reserve the cooking liquid; discard the bay leaf. Put the carrots in a blender with 6 tablespoons of the reserved cooking liquid and liquidise until smooth. Return the carrot cream to the saucepan, re-heat and season well. Spoon into a warmed serving bowl.

Cut the courgette and nut roast into squares, arrange on a warmed platter and garnish with watercress. Serve with the hot carrot cream.

PEASANT BAKED TOMATOES

SERVES 4

4 very large or beef tomatoes
1 × 7 oz (200 g) tin tuna in brine or 2 × 4½ oz (120 g) tins sardines in oil,
drained
4 tablespoons wholemeal breadcrumbs
1 tablespoon sunflower oil
1 tablespoon chopped fresh or 1 teaspoon dried basil
1 clove garlic, crushed
Juice of 1 lemon
Freshly ground black pepper
2 oz (50 g) Edam cheese, grated
Salad leaves or watercress to garnish

• Serve these stuffed tomatoes with sweet potatoes – they are wonderful baked in their skins, cooked just like regular jacket potatoes.

Pre-heat the oven to gas mark 6, 400°F (200°C).

Cut the tomatoes in half and, using a teaspoon, scoop out the seeds, pulp and juice into a bowl. Add the tuna or sardines, half the breadcrumbs, the oil, basil, garlic, lemon juice and pepper. Mash well with a fork and taste: adjust the seasoning if necessary.

Place the tomato shells, cut side up, on a baking sheet. Spoon in the fish mixture and sprinkle each filled tomato with the grated cheese and remaining breadcrumbs. Bake in the oven for 10 minutes until golden-brown on top and bubbling hot. Using a fish slice, transfer the tomatoes to a warmed serving dish, garnish with salad leaves or watercress and serve at once.

COUSCOUS WARMER

SERVES 4

1 tablespoon sunflower oil
1 large onion, chopped
1 clove garlic, crushed
1 teaspoon ground cumin
1/2 teaspoon ground ginger
2 carrots, sliced
2 parsnips, peeled and sliced
1 aubergine, cubed
1 medium potato, cubed
4 oz (100 g) cabbage, shredded
2 tomatoes, chopped
Freshly ground black pepper
5 oz (150 g) cooked chick peas
3 oz (75 g) sultanas
8 oz (225 g) couscous

FOR THE TOPPING:
1 hard-boiled egg, finely chopped
2 tablespoons chopped parsley
Grated rind 1 lemon

● This dish is really aromatic and deliciously satisfying. The couscous available in this country is nearly always pre-cooked and will need only soaking and heating gently – just follow the instructions on the packet.

Heat the oil in a large pan. Fry the onion until golden, then add the garlic and spices and fry gently for a further minute. Add the vegetables and enough water to cover and season well. Add the cooked chick peas and sultanas and simmer for 20–30 minutes or until the vegetables are tender.

Meanwhile, cook the couscous according to the instructions on the packet. In a bowl mix together the chopped egg, parsley and lemon rind.

Pile the hot couscous on to a warmed platter and spoon over the vegetables. Scatter with the egg and parsley topping and serve at once.

WARM SALAD WITH CHICKEN LIVERS & APPLES

SERVES 4

1 large cos lettuce, washed and separated into leaves
1 lb (450 g) chicken livers
1 tablespoon sunflower oil
2 dessert apples, cored and thinly sliced
Freshly ground black pepper
½ bunch spring onions, chopped

FOR THE LOW CAL DRESSING:
Grated rind and juice 1 orange
1 tablespoon sunflower oil
5 fl oz (150 ml) natural yoghurt
2 tablespoons semi-skimmed milk
Freshly ground black pepper
Chopped fresh herbs (optional)

● This salad is really delicious. Serve it with plenty of warm granary bread.

Combine the low cal dressing ingredients in a bowl. Place the cos lettuce leaves in a large salad bowl, tearing any large leaves into pieces. Pour over the low cal dressing, toss and set aside.

Trim and wash the chicken livers, pat dry with kitchen paper and cut each one in half. Heat the oil in a large frying-pan or wok. Add the livers and fry over a medium heat for about 4 minutes, turning once or twice, until just cooked through. Add the sliced apples to the frying-pan and toss together with the livers for a further 2 minutes. Grind over some black pepper and sprinkle with the chopped spring onions.

Spoon the chicken liver and apple mixture over the lettuce and serve at once.

PASTA, SPINACH & TUNA SALAD WITH TOMATO DRESSING

SERVES 4

FOR THE SALAD:
5 oz (150 g) wholemeal pasta shapes
5 oz (150 g) green pasta shapes
4 oz (100 g) fresh spinach
1 tablespoon sunflower oil
1 × 7 oz (200 g) tin tuna fish in brine, drained and flaked
Freshly ground black pepper
3 tomatoes, chopped, to garnish

FOR THE TOMATO DRESSING:
10 fl oz (300 ml) tomato juice
1 tablespoon tomato purée
Pinch cayenne pepper
Dash Worcestershire sauce
4 tablespoons chopped parsley
1 tablespoon chopped fresh basil
1 tablespoon sunflower oil
2 cloves garlic, crushed
Freshly ground black pepper

• The raw spinach in this salad gives a good texture and flavour. But remember that when cooking pasta it's always better to undercook it slightly so that it remains firm to the bite.

Cook the pasta in plenty of boiling water according to the packet instructions, taking care not to overcook it. Drain and refresh under cold running water (this prevents further cooking). Leave it in a colander to drain.

Remove the stems from the spinach and discard. Wash the leaves well. Roll the leaves into tight bundles and shred finely with a knife.

Now make the tomato dressing. In a small saucepan simmer all the dressing ingredients together for 3 minutes. Remove from the heat and allow to cool, then taste and adjust the seasoning if necessary.

In a large serving bowl toss together the cooked pasta, oil, flaked tuna and three quarters of the spinach. Season to taste. Pour over the tomato dressing. Scatter the remaining spinach around the edge of the dish. Sprinkle with the chopped tomatoes and grind over more black pepper.

SWEET & SPICED POTATO SALAD

SERVES 4

2 lb (1 kg) unpeeled potatoes, washed and cut into 2 inch (5 cm) chunks
1 teaspoon ground turmeric
1 lb (450 g) parsnips, peeled and cut into 2 inch (5 cm) chunks
4 thin slices lean ham, shredded
Salad leaves to garnish

FOR THE DRESSING:
1 small onion, finely chopped
1 teaspoon curry powder or paste
4 oz (100 g) low-fat cream cheese
5 fl oz (150 ml) semi-skimmed milk
Pinch ground nutmeg
Freshly ground black pepper

• Try to use waxy potatoes for this recipe as they tend to be firmer and have a better texture.

Put the potatoes in a saucepan with the turmeric. Cover with cold water and a lid. Bring to a rapid boil, add the parsnips and cook for 10 minutes or until the vegetables are just tender

Meanwhile, make the dressing. In a small bowl mix together the onion, curry powder or paste and cream cheese. Gradually stir in the milk and season with nutmeg and black pepper. Taste and adjust the seasoning as necessary.

Drain the vegetables well and toss in the dressing while they are still hot. Put them on a large platter, scatter the shredded ham over and surround with plenty of salad leaves.

RICE, LENTIL & CHILLI SALAD

SERVES 4

5 oz (150 g) brown rice
5 oz (150 g) red lentils, picked over
8 oz (225 g) fresh or frozen runner beans, cooked
4 slices salami, chopped
Chopped parsley to garnish

FOR THE DRESSING:
1 clove garlic, crushed
1/2 tablespoon ground coriander
5 fl oz (150 ml) water
1/2 vegetable stock cube
Pinch chilli powder or *cayenne pepper*
5 fl oz (150 ml) natural yoghurt
1 teaspoon honey (optional)

● You can adapt this delicious rice dish by using smoked mackerel fillets instead of salami.

Wash the rice and lentils. Bring a large pan of water to the boil, add the rice, cover and cook for 10 minutes. Add the lentils and continue cooking for a further 15–20 minutes or until both are just tender. Drain well and leave in a colander to cool.

Next make the dressing. In a saucepan heat the garlic and coriander over a medium heat for 30 seconds. Pour in the water and add the ½ stock cube and chilli powder or cayenne pepper. Stir until smooth, remove from the heat and allow to cool for 5 minutes. Stir in the yoghurt and honey (if using) and season to taste.

In a large bowl combine the rice, lentils and cooked runner beans. Pour over the dressing, pile into a salad bowl and scatter with the chopped salami and parsley.

CRACKED WHEAT SALAD WITH MUSTARD DRESSING

SERVES 4

6 oz (175 g) cracked wheat
1 onion, chopped
4 tablespoons chopped parsley
3 large carrots, peeled and grated
1 packet alfalfa sprouts, washed and drained, or *3 punnets mustard and cress*
Freshly ground black pepper

FOR THE TOPPING:
1 tablespoon poppy seeds
2 hard-boiled eggs, chopped
Chopped parsley

FOR THE MUSTARD DRESSING:
2 tablespoons mild or coarse mustard
Freshly ground black pepper
Juice 2 lemons
4 tablespoons sunflower oil
1 clove garlic, crushed
3 tablespoons cold water

• Cracked wheat, sometimes known as bulgur wheat, doesn't need any cooking, just soaking. It has a nutty, crunchy texture and makes a great salad ingredient. Serve this salad with baked jacket potatoes.

Cover the cracked wheat with cold water and soak for 15–20 minutes, then drain and squeeze out the excess water.

Put the poppy seeds for the topping in a small saucepan and heat over a medium heat for 2 minutes or until roasted. Set aside.

In a small bowl toss together all the dressing ingredients. Season to taste.

In a large bowl toss all the salad ingredients together with the mustard dressing and season to taste. Pile the salad into a large dish and sprinkle over the topping ingredients.

PIZZA SALAD

SERVES 4

FOR THE PIZZA BASE:
1 large onion, sliced
½ teaspoon ground nutmeg
5 oz (150 g) self-raising wholemeal flour
5 oz (150 g) plain flour
Pinch salt
A little semi-skimmed milk
1 tablespoon sunflower oil
2 oz (50 g) Edam cheese, grated

FOR THE TOPPING:
1 bunch radishes, sliced
5 tomatoes, roughly chopped
2 punnets mustard and cress
½ cucumber, diced
Freshly ground black pepper
A little lemon juice
Garlic, finely chopped (optional)
2 oz (50 g) Edam cheese, grated, to garnish

• This makes a change from the usual pizza with a cooked topping, and you can, of course, use a different combination of salad ingredients from those suggested.

Pre-heat the oven to gas mark 6, 400°F (200°C).

Put the sliced onion and nutmeg in a small saucepan. Add 3 tablespoons water, cover and cook gently for 5 minutes. Remove from the heat and allow to cool.

In a large mixing bowl, sift the flours and salt and add enough semi-skimmed milk to bind the dough. Knead for 10 seconds and roll out on a floured board or work-surface into a large rectangle or round, the thickness of a 50p piece. Place on a greased baking sheet and, using a fork, prick the dough all over and crimp the edges. Brush the top with sunflower oil and sprinkle over the softened onions and grated cheese. Bake in the oven for 10–15 minutes or until the pastry is golden brown.

Meanwhile, prepare the salad ingredients for the topping and place in a bowl. Season with black pepper and lemon juice and a little finely chopped garlic (if using).

Remove the cooked pizza base from the oven, carefully transfer from the baking sheet to a large platter or chopping board and pile on the seasoned salad. Sprinkle with the cheese and serve at once.

HOT TACO SALAD

SERVES 4

1¹/₂ lb (750 g) unpeeled potatoes, washed and cut in half
1 tablespoon sunflower oil
1 × 7 oz (200 g) tin butter beans, drained
1 medium onion, chopped
1 teaspoon Tabasco sauce
1 garlic clove, crushed
1 × 14 oz (400 g) tin tomatoes
1 teaspoon dried basil
Freshly ground black pepper
¹/₂ Iceberg lettuce
¹/₂ cucumber, sliced
3 oz (75 g) taco chips
1 punnet mustard and cress

FOR THE SAUCE:
5 fl oz (150 ml) natural yoghurt
2 teaspoons ground coriander
1 teaspoon tomato purée
1 clove garlic, crushed
1 tablespoon curd cheese
Freshly ground black pepper

● This hot salad makes a substantial main meal. Don't peel the potatoes – just wash and scrub them well.

Place the potatoes in a pan, cover with cold water, put the lid on the pan and boil for about 15 minutes or until just tender. Drain well and slice thickly.

Pre-heat the oven to gas mark 5, 375°F (190°C).

Heat the oil in a saucepan, add the beans, onion, Tabasco and garlic and cook gently for 3 minutes. Add the tomatoes and basil, bring to the boil and simmer for 10 minutes. Then add the sliced potatoes, season to taste and transfer to a casserole or ovenproof dish. Cover and bake in the oven for 20 minutes.

Meanwhile, prepare the salad. Tear the lettuce into pieces and toss with the cucumber. Mix together the sauce ingredients, seasoning to taste.

Divide the salad equally between 4 dinner plates. Spoon the hot potato mixture on to the centre of each, drizzle over the sauce, surround with the taco chips and scatter with the mustard and cress. Serve at once.

BAKING

TIPS

- Try using different grains, flakes and seeds – there are many varieties.

- Wholemeal and granary flour are readily available now. They give a lovely nutty flavour and help increase fibre intake.

- Season your baking with dried or fresh fruit, nuts, herbs, seeds, vegetables, essences, spices – the flavourings are endless.

- Use low-fat dairy products in baking like yoghurt, skimmed or semi-skimmed milk, low-fat cream cheese and buttermilk.

- Dried and fresh yeast are simple to use, but I prefer easy-blend yeast which is even easier and reliable.

- Remember, when adding liquid to a baking powder or soda bread dough, to mix quickly as the raising agent starts working immediately.

- When a recipe calls for plain flour, try using unbleached flour which looks the same and works similarly but is much better for you (it is enriched with iron and other minerals) and tastes better. It is available in all leading supermarkets.

MUSTARD CELERY GANNET

MAKES 1 × 2 lb (1 kg) LOAF

A little sunflower oil for greasing
14 oz (400 g) self-raising wholemeal flour, plus extra for dusting
1 teaspoon bicarbonate of soda
Good pinch salt
4 sticks celery
4 oz (100 g) Edam or low-fat Cheddar-type cheese, grated
Freshly ground black pepper
1 tablespoon French mustard
10 fl oz (300 ml) semi-skimmed milk

● Use French or wholegrain mustard for this delicious moist bread.

Pre-heat the oven to gas mark 7, 425°F (220°C). Grease a 2 lb (1 kg) loaf tin.

Sift the flour, bicarbonate of soda and salt together. Chop the celery sticks and leaves finely and add with the cheese to the flour. Grind in some black pepper.

In a large jug combine the mustard and milk and gradually add to the dry ingredients. Mix with a fork and, using your hands, bring the mixture into a soft ball. Knead on a floured board or work-surface for 30 seconds. Shape into an oblong, place in the prepared tin, sprinkle with a little flour and bake in the oven for 45 minutes. Turn out and cool on a wire rack.

SPRING ONION SWISS ROLL

MAKES 2 × 8 oz (225 g) LOAVES

1 teaspoon dried thyme
2 tablespoons chopped parsley
1 bunch spring onions, chopped
11 oz (300 g) wholemeal flour, plus extra for dusting
2 teaspoons baking powder
Pinch salt
10 fl oz (300 ml) water
2 tablespoons sunflower oil
1 small egg, beaten

● A quick substantial bread, excellent with soups and casseroles.

Pre-heat the oven to gas mark 5, 375°F, (190°C).

In a small bowl mix the herbs and spring onions. Set to one side.

In a large bowl sift together the flour, baking powder and salt. Combine the water and oil, pour into the flour and mix well. Turn on to a floured board or work-surface and knead for 10 seconds. Roll out into a rectangle ½ inch (1 cm) thick. Sprinkle the herb mixture over the dough and roll up at each end, until the two rolls meet. Using a sharp knife, cut between the rolls to separate them. Pinch the edges together.

Place the rolls on a floured baking sheet and brush with the beaten egg. Sprinkle with a little flour and bake in the oven for 30 minutes. Allow them to cool on a wire rack before slicing thickly to serve.

SEEDY BREAD

MAKES 2 × 1 lb (450 g) LOAVES

A little sunflower oil for greasing
8 oz (225 g) wholemeal flour
8 oz (225 g) granary flour
Pinch salt
1 oz (25 g) sesame seeds
1 oz (25 g) poppy seeds
1 teaspoon brown sugar
1 sachet easy-blend yeast
10–15 fl oz (300–400 ml) warm water
1 tablespoon porridge oats

● A basic bread dough can be mixed and flavoured with all different kinds of ingredients. This seedy bread has a lovely nutty flavour and crunchy texture.

Pre-heat the oven to gas mark 6, 400°F (200°C).

Lightly grease 2 × 5 inch (13 cm) cake tins.

Sift together the flours and salt and add the seeds, sugar and yeast. Pour in the water and mix to a soft dough. Transfer to a lightly floured board or work-surface and knead for 2 minutes.

Divide the dough in half and place each piece in a cake tin. Cover with cling film and leave in a warm place (such as an airing cupboard or a warm spot in the kitchen) for 30 minutes or until the dough doubles in size. Brush the top with water and sprinkle with porridge oats. Bake in the oven for 30 minutes. Turn out and cool on a wire rack.

HERB & POPPY OATCAKES

MAKES 12

8 oz (225 g) medium oatmeal, plus extra for dusting
2 oz (50 g) wholemeal flour, plus extra for dusting
½ teaspoon bicarbonate of soda
Pinch salt
1 teaspoon dried mixed herbs
2 oz (50 g) vegetable margarine
1 egg white, beaten
1 tablespoon poppy seeds

● These are excellent served for breakfast – or at any time for that matter. I love them spread thinly with peanut butter and topped with slices of cucumber and freshly ground black pepper.

Pre-heat the oven to gas mark 5, 375°F (190°C).

In a bowl sift together the oatmeal, flour, bicarbonate of soda and salt and add the herbs.

In a pan over a low heat, melt the margarine and pour this over the oat mixture. Blend well and, using a fork, gradually mix in enough boiling water to make a fairly moist dough.

Tip the dough out on to a floured board or work-surface. Sprinkle with oatmeal and knead lightly. Divide the dough in half and roll each piece into a circle about ¼ inch (5 mm) thick, then cut each circle into 6 triangular oatcakes and dust with oatmeal.

Place the oatcakes on a floured baking sheet, brush with the beaten egg white and sprinkle over the poppy seeds. Bake in the oven for 20–25 minutes, turning the cakes over several times, until dry and crisp. Cool on a wire rack and serve warm or cold.

ITALIAN THYME BREAD

MAKES 1 LARGE ROUND LOAF

8 oz (225 g) wholemeal flour, plus extra for dusting
8 oz (225 g) granary flour
1 sachet easy-blend yeast
Freshly ground black pepper
10 fl oz (300 ml) warm water
1 tablespoon sunflower oil
2 tablespoons chopped fresh thyme
1 tablespoon coarse rock salt

• This wonderful, flat, Italian peasant bread isn't meant to be a perfect round loaf. It doesn't matter if the shape looks odd – it's the nature of the beast! To ring the changes you can use various different herbs to flavour the bread instead of thyme. Serve it with soups and stews.

Sift the flours into a bowl and mix in the yeast and black pepper. Pour in the warm water and oil and mix with a fork until you have a rough dough. Tip the dough out on to a floured board or work-surface and knead well for 5 minutes or until smooth and springy. Place the dough in a clean bowl, cover with cling film and leave to rise in a warm place for 1½ hours.

Pre-heat the oven to gas mark 6, 400°F (200°C). Sprinkle the risen dough with the thyme and knead again on a lightly floured surface. Roll the dough out into a large 10 inch (25 cm) circle. Place on a floured baking sheet and prick the top all over with a fork. Cover and allow to rise again for 10 minutes before baking. Brush the top with water and sprinkle over the rock salt. Bake in the oven for 35 minutes or until golden-brown and crisp.

SAGE & MUSHROOM MUFFINS

MAKES 12

1 teaspoon sunflower oil, plus extra for greasing
4 oz (100 g) mushrooms, chopped
½ teaspoon dried sage
4 oz (100 g) wholemeal flour, plus extra for dusting
4 oz (100 g) plain flour
2 teaspoons baking powder
1 large egg
5 fl oz (150 ml) semi-skimmed milk
3 tablespoons natural yoghurt
Freshly ground black pepper

● American muffins make great snacks. Serve these with soups, salads or almost any other savoury dish.

Pre-heat the oven to gas mark 6, 400°F (200°C).

Heat the oil in a frying-pan, put in the mushrooms and sage and fry over a high heat for 2 minutes to evaporate any excess water. Remove from the heat and set aside to cool.

Grease and flour a patty tin with 12 indentations. Sift the flours into a bowl with the baking powder.

In a jug beat together the cooled mushrooms, egg, milk, yoghurt and black pepper. Pour this into the flour mixture and beat quickly.

Three-quarters-fill the patty tin with the mixture and bake in the oven for 15–20 minutes or until golden. Remove from the oven, turn out and serve hot.

SEEDY BISCUITS

MAKES 12 BISCUITS

8 oz (225 g) wholemeal flour, plus extra for dusting
1 teaspoon baking powder
2 tablespoons sesame seeds
2 tablespoons soy sauce
2 tablespoons sunflower oil
4 tablespoons semi-skimmed milk, plus extra for brushing
1 tablespoon carraway seeds

● Particularly good eaten with warm hummus or curd cheese with a salad.

Pre-heat the oven to gas mark 6, 400°F (200°C).
Sift the flour with the baking powder and add the sesame seeds. Mix in the soy sauce, oil and just enough milk to form a soft dough. Form into a ball, then roll out thinly on a lightly floured board or work-surface. Prick all over with a fork. Cut into 4 inch (10 cm) squares. Place on a floured baking sheet, brush lightly with milk and sprinkle with carraway seeds. Bake in the oven for 12–15 minutes or until golden-brown. Cool on a wire rack.

CHAPATI

MAKES 4

8 oz (225 g) wholemeal flour, plus extra for dusting
2 teaspoons curry powder
Freshly ground black pepper
5 fl oz (150 ml) warm water

● The basic Indian unleavened bread – serve as a wholesome accompaniment to any meal.

In a bowl sift the flour, curry powder and black pepper together and mix in enough warm water to make a soft dough. Knead for 2 minutes, then cover with cling film and leave to stand for 30 minutes. Divide the dough into 4 equal pieces and roll each one into a thin pancake.

Heat a non-stick frying-pan until hot. Sprinkle in a little flour and if it turns brown straight away the pan is hot enough to use. Cook the chapatis in the pan one at a time for approximately 30 seconds on each side or until blister-like bubbles appear and they are lightly coloured. Serve at once.

MUESLI COOKIES

MAKES 10–12

4 oz (100 g) vegetable margarine, plus extra for greasing
3 oz (75 g) self-raising wholemeal flour, plus extra for dusting
1 teaspoon ground mixed spice
2 tablespoons brown sugar
1 large egg, beaten
5 oz (150 g) muesli
2 oz (50 g) sultanas
2 oz (50 g) unsalted peanuts, chopped

• Look out for this type of muesli biscuit the next time you are in a Hearty Eater restaurant.

Pre-heat the oven to gas mark 4, 350°F (180°C). Lightly grease and flour two baking sheets.

In a bowl beat together the margarine, spice and sugar. Gradually add the egg, beating well. Add the flour, muesli, sultanas and peanuts and mix thoroughly. Place tablespoons of the mixture on the prepared baking sheets and flatten with fork. Bake in the oven for 15–20 minutes or until golden. Remove from the oven and allow to cool on the baking sheets for 2 minutes (this allows the biscuits to harden slightly); then, using a fish slice, transfer the biscuits to a wire rack to finish cooling.

WHOLEMEAL PRUNE SCONES

MAKES 6 SCONES

4 oz (100 g) plain flour, plus extra for dusting
4 oz (100 g) wholemeal flour
4 level teaspoons baking powder
1 oz (25 g) vegetable margarine
3 oz (75 g) pre-soaked prunes, chopped
About 5 fl oz (150 ml) semi-skimmed milk, plus extra for brushing
1 tablespoon bran

• The secret of successful scones is to prepare them as quickly as possible, handle the dough as little as you can and cook them in a very hot oven.

Pre-heat the oven to gas mark 7, 425°F (220°C).

Sift the flours and baking powder into a mixing bowl and stir well. Using your fingertips rub in the margarine and stir in the chopped prunes. Pour in enough milk to make a firm but not sticky dough, stir with a fork, then bring the dough together using your hands.

Transfer the dough to a lightly floured board or work-surface and knead quickly for 10 seconds. Turn the dough over and shape and pat out to a small round ¾ inch (2 cm) thick. Using a floured 4 inch (10 cm) round cutter, cut out 6 rounds. Place the scones on a floured baking sheet, brush with milk and sprinkle with the bran. Bake in the oven for 12–15 minutes or until well risen.

MUESLI CAKE

MAKES 1 × 2 lb (1 kg) LOAF

4 oz (100 g) dried figs, chopped
5 fl oz (150 ml) orange juice
12 oz (350 g) wholemeal flour
2 oz (50 g) plain flour, plus extra for dusting
4 oz (100 g) muesli
1 sachet easy-blend yeast
5 fl oz (150 ml) warm water
a little sunflower oil for greasing
1 egg, beaten
1 tablespoon porridge oats

• Serve this at teatime or pop a slice in your lunch box.

Soak the figs in the orange juice for 30 minutes. In a large bowl sift together the flours and stir in the muesli and yeast. Mix in the water, orange juice and figs. Turn the dough out on to a floured board or work-surface and knead for 5 minutes, adding a little more water if the dough is too dry. Put the dough in a large clean bowl and cover with cling film. Leave in a warm place to rise for 1 hour or until doubled in size.

Pre-heat the oven to gas mark 7, 425°F (220°C). Lightly grease a 2 lb (1 kg) loaf tin or deep cake tin.

Knead the risen dough quickly until smooth. Shape it into a loaf and place in the prepared tin. Cover and leave to stand for 15 minutes or until well risen. Brush with beaten egg, scatter over the oats and bake in the oven for 30–40 minutes. Cool on a wire rack.

PUDDINGS

TIPS

• When using wholemeal flour for pastry, you may find that you need to add extra water as the flour tends to absorb more.

• Try to use fruits which are in season – they are then at their best and cheapest.

• Spices like cinnamon, nutmeg and ginger are healthier than sugar as flavourings for puddings.

• Use low-fat natural yoghurt or flavoured yoghurts rather than cream to accompany your puddings.

• Using dried fruit in your puddings means that you can cut down or, better still, cut out sugar.

• If you need to use sugar, use natural types like muscovado (unrefined), molasses or honey. These sugars are much better for you, but take care – they are just as calorific.

• Nuts and seeds can be high in calories but are rich in protein, vitamins and minerals and, used sensibly, give an excellent texture and flavour to puddings.

MA'S THROW-IT-TOGETHER PUD

SERVES 4

A little sunflower oil for greasing
5 thick slices left-over wholemeal bread, soaked in cold water
1 tablespoon plain flour
1 teaspoon baking powder
2 tablespoons porridge oats
2 tablespoons honey
1 egg white
3 oz (75 g) sultanas
1 apple, grated
1 pear, grated
1 teaspoon ground mixed spice
1/2 teaspoon ground nutmeg

● This adaptation of a recipe of my mother's is a great way of using up stale bread and fruit which has seen better days. Serve warm with natural yoghurt as a pudding, or on its own for a teatime treat.

Pre-heat the oven to gas mark 5, 375°F (190°C). Lightly oil an ovenproof dish.

Squeeze the water from the bread and place the bread in a large mixing bowl. Add the remaining ingredients and combine thoroughly. Pour into the ovenproof dish and bake in the oven for 1 hour or until firm and golden-brown on top.

WARM PEAR & MUSCOVADO FLAN

SERVES 4

8 oz (225 g) Wholemeal Shortcrust Pastry (see page 63)
5 ripe dessert pears
3 ripe bananas, mashed to a purée
2 oz (50 g) muscovado sugar

● The muscovado sugar and pears give a wonderful flavour to this flan.

Pre-heat the oven to gas mark 6, 400°F (200°C).

Line an 8 inch (20 cm) flan tin or dish with the pastry, prick the base well with a fork and chill in the refrigerator for 15 minutes to allow the pastry to relax (this will prevent it from shrinking during cooking). Remove from the refrigerator, place a circle of greasproof paper inside and half-fill with uncooked rice, pasta or dried beans. Then bake in the oven for 15–20 minutes.

Meanwhile, peel, core and slice 2 of the pears and cook in a covered saucepan with 6 tablespoons cold water for about 10 minutes or until soft. Mash the pears with a fork until smooth, then stir into the banana purée.

Take the pastry case out of the oven and remove the paper and rice. Spoon the pear filling into the pastry case. Peel, core and slice the remaining pears and arrange, slightly overlapping, on top of the filling. Sprinkle over the muscovado sugar, return the flan to the oven and bake for 15 minutes. Serve hot or warm.

APRICOT YOGHURT ICE-CREAM

SERVES 4

1 × 14 oz (400 g) tin apricots in natural juice
1 pint (600 ml) set natural yoghurt
2 drops almond essence (optional)

• This ice-cream is very simple to prepare. It goes well with all puddings and is delicious served with fresh fruit.

Drain the apricots, reserving the juice. Liquidise or mash the fruit to a smooth pulp. In a large bowl mix together the apricot pulp and yoghurt and add 4 tablespoons of the reserved apricot juice and the almond essence (if using). Turn the mixture into a lidded freezer container, cover and freeze until solid.

Transfer the ice-cream to the refrigerator 30 minutes before serving to soften it slightly.

SEEDY FRUIT CRUMBLE

SERVES 4

2 lb (1 kg) ripe pears, peeled, cored and cut into chunks
4 oz (100 g) pre-soaked dried apricots, chopped
Juice 2 oranges

FOR THE TOPPING:
4 oz (100 g) wholemeal flour
2 oz (50 g) vegetable margarine
1 oz (25 g) porridge oats
1 oz (25 g) sesame seeds
1 oz (25 g) sunflower seeds
1 oz (25 g) muscovado sugar

• Fruit crumbles always go down well. You can use plums, apples or rhubarb in place of the pears.

Pre-heat the oven to gas mark 6, 400°F (200°C).
Pile the pear chunks into an ovenproof dish and sprinkle the chopped apricots on top. Pour over the orange juice.
Now make the topping. Sift the flour into a large bowl and rub in the margarine. Mix in the oats, seeds and sugar and sprinkle over the fruit. Bake in the oven for 35 minutes or until the fruit is tender and the topping is golden-brown.

CARROT & GINGER PUDDING WITH ORANGE SAUCE

SERVES 4

A little sunflower oil for greasing
3 oz (75 g) porridge oats
4 oz (100 g) wholemeal breadcrumbs
6 oz (175 g) carrots, grated
2 oz (50 g) ground almonds
1 teaspoon ground ginger
1/2 teaspoon ground nutmeg
Grated rind and juice 2 oranges
4 oz (100 g) sultanas
5 fl oz (150 ml) natural yoghurt
3 egg whites
Orange segments to garnish

FOR THE ORANGE SAUCE:
5 fl oz (150 ml) natural yoghurt
1 × 7 oz (200 g) tin frozen concentrated orange juice

● A delicious, warming pudding for cold winter days.

Oil a 1½ pint (900 ml) pudding basin.

In a bowl combine all the pudding ingredients except the egg whites and orange segments. Whisk the egg whites until stiff, then fold them into the carrot mixture. Put the mixture into the pudding basin, cover the top with aluminium foil and tie securely with string.

Stand the pudding in a saucepan containing enough boiling water to come half-way up the sides of the basin. Cover the pan with a tight-fitting lid and boil for 1½ hours. Top up with boiling water as needed.

Meanwhile, make the sauce. Simply mix the ingredients together and chill in the refrigerator.

When the pudding is cooked, remove the string and foil from the basin. Slide a knife around the outside of the pudding to loosen it and turn out on to a large warmed plate. Decorate with the orange segments and serve with the orange sauce handed seperately.

SPICED PLUM PIZZA

SERVES 4

FOR THE PIZZA BASE:

A little sunflower oil for greasing
4 oz (100 g) wholemeal flour
4 oz (100 g) plain flour
1 heaped teaspoon baking powder
2 dessert apples, cored and grated
5 fl oz (150 ml) semi-skimmed milk

FOR THE TOPPING:

1 tablespoon porridge oats
1 lb (450 g) plums, stoned and quartered
2 tablespoons muscovado sugar
1 teaspoon ground mixed spice

● Pizzas don't always need to be savoury. Serve this delicious sweet one topped with yoghurt.

Pre-heat the oven to gas mark 7, 425°F (220°C). Lightly oil a pizza tray or baking sheet.

Sift the flours and baking powder together in a bowl and add the grated apples and milk. Mix with a fork to form a soft dough. Knead on a floured board or work-surface for 30 seconds.

Roll out the dough into a round ¼ inch (5 mm) thick. Place on the prepared pizza tray or baking sheet, prick all over with a fork and crimp the edge of the pizza using thumb and fingers.

Scatter the pizza base with the porridge oats and spoon over the plums. Sprinkle with the sugar and mixed spice. Bake in the oven for 20 minutes or until the plums are soft and bubbling and the base crisp and cooked. Serve immediately.

FRUIT KEBABS

SERVES 4

2 bananas, peeled and cut into thick rounds
2 red apples, cored and quartered
2 oranges, peeled, segmented and pith removed
12 pre-soaked dried prunes
8 tinned apricot halves, drained
1 tablespoon runny honey

FOR THE SAUCE:
Grated rind and juice 2 oranges
2 tablespoons apple juice
1/2 oz (15 g) porridge oats
Pinch ground nutmeg

- Children love this quick, easy and very attractive pudding.

Divide the fruit between 4 skewers, alternating the 5 types.

In a bowl mix together the sauce ingredients and pour over the fruit kebabs.

Pre-heat the grill. Trickle the honey over the kebabs and place under the grill for 3–5 minutes or until the fruit and oats are well browned. Serve at once.

HOT APRICOT SOUFFLÉ

SERVES 4

A little sunflower oil for greasing
8 oz (225 g) dried apricots, soaked in water overnight and drained
10 fl oz (300 ml) water
2 oz (50 g) muscovado sugar
5 egg whites

- Dried prunes make a good alternative to apricots in this recipe. When folding in the egg whites, use a large metal spoon as this way you're less likely to knock out too much air.

Pre-heat the oven to gas mark 5, 375°F (190°C). Lightly grease a 2 pint (1.2 litre) soufflé or deep ovenproof dish.

Cook the apricots in the water for 10–15 minutes or until very soft, then mash or liquidise until very smooth. Stir in half the sugar.

In a large dry bowl whisk the egg whites until stiff. Beat in the remaining sugar and fold into the apricot purée. Pour the mixture carefully into the soufflé dish and bake in the oven for 15–20 minutes or until risen and set. Serve at once.

FRESH FRUIT RICE PUDDING

SERVES 4

8 oz (225 g) brown rice
4 oz (100 g) sultanas
1 bay leaf
½ teaspoon ground ginger
2 pears, cored and sliced
About 1 pint (600 ml) skimmed or semi-skimmed milk
2 bananas, peeled and sliced
2 oranges, peeled, segmented and pith removed
2 oz (50 g) blackberries or black grapes

- Use any fruits which are in season for this pudding. Either short- or long-grain brown rice is suitable. Serve topped with yoghurt.

Put the rice, sultanas, bay leaf, ginger, pears and milk in a saucepan. Cover with a lid and bring to the boil. Simmer gently for 35–40 minutes or until the rice is tender, adding a little extra milk if the pan looks as if it might dry out.

Remove from the heat, stir in the remaining fruits and serve hot, warm or chilled.

OATMEAL FLUMMERY

SERVES 4

3 oz (75 g) fine oatmeal
¹/₂ teaspoon ground cinnamon
6 oz (175 g) black grapes, halved and de-pipped
10 fl oz (300 ml) natural yoghurt
Honey or *concentrated apple juice to taste*
2 oz (50 g) hazelnuts, chopped

● Here's a simple pudding, using oats, yoghurt and fruit. Try it at breakfast time too as an interesting change from regular porridge.

Toast the oatmeal in a dry frying-pan on top of the stove until lightly browned. Then stir in the cinnamon and allow to cool.

In a bowl gently mix the grapes with the yoghurt and sweeten to taste with honey or apple juice. Stir in three quarters of the toasted oats.

Spoon into individual glasses, sprinkle with the remaining oatmeal and top with the chopped hazelnuts.

PLUM BROWN BETTY

SERVES 4

A little sunflower oil for greasing
8 slices wholemeal bread, crusts removed
1 tablespoon ground cinnamon
2 lb (1 kg) plums, stoned and quartered
2 tablespoons runny honey

● This is an old English pudding. You can use gooseberries, apples or rhubarb instead of plums. Serve hot with natural yoghurt flavoured with vanilla or yoghurt ice-cream (see page 106).

Pre-heat the oven to gas mark 6, 400°F (200°C). Lightly oil a 1½ pint (900 ml) pie dish or deep cake tin.

Sprinkle both sides of each bread slice with cinnamon. Trim 1 slice so that it fits the base of the dish or tin. Put a thick layer of fruit on top and trickle some honey and cinnamon over it. Add another layer of bread, plums, honey and cinnamon and arrange a final layer of bread slices slightly overlapping to cover the fruit. Drizzle some honey over and bake in the oven for 30–40 minutes or until golden-brown.

Serve straight from the dish or run a knife round the outside of the pudding and turn it out on to a warmed plate.

APPLE, HONEY
& BANANA BREAD PUDDING

SERVES 4

A little sunflower oil for greasing
4 large slices wholemeal bread
4 tablespoons runny honey
1 oz (25 g) sultanas
2 bananas, peeled and sliced
15 fl oz (450 ml) semi-skimmed milk
3 eggs
Few drops vanilla essence
2 dessert apples, cored and thinly sliced
Ground nutmeg and cinnamon

● This, without doubt, is one of my favourites. To taste this banana pudding at its best, serve it hot or warm.

Pre-heat the oven to gas mark 5, 375°C (190°C). Lightly oil an ovenproof dish.

Spread the bread with a little of the honey and cut into quarters (don't remove the crusts). Place in the ovenproof dish and sprinkle with the sultanas and sliced bananas.

Combine the milk, eggs and remaining honey in a bowl and beat well. Add a few drops of vanilla essence to the milk mixture and strain over the bread. Arrange the sliced apples on the top and sprinkle generously with ground nutmeg and cinnamon. Bake in the oven for 25–30 minutes or until set and golden-brown.

PLUM & BLACKCURRANT PANCAKE PIE

SERVES 4

FOR THE PANCAKE BATTER:
2 oz (50 g) wholemeal flour
5 fl oz (150 ml) semi-skimmed milk
2 teaspoons ground cinnamon
1 egg
1 teaspoon sunflower oil, plus extra for greasing

FOR THE FILLING:
1 lb (450 g) plums, stoned and quartered
1 × 7 oz (200 g) tin unsweetened blackcurrants, drained and juice reserved
1 teaspoon ground cinnamon
4 oz (100 g) low-fat cream or curd cheese
10 fl oz (300 ml) natural yoghurt
Vanilla essence to taste

- A lovely combination of fruits, cream cheese and cinnamon pancakes.

First make the pancakes. In a large bowl, combine the flour, milk, cinnamon, egg and oil. Beat well until smooth.

Heat a non-stick frying-pan. Add a little oil and wipe it round the pan with kitchen paper so that the base is completely coated. Pour in enough batter to coat the base of the pan, cook for 1 minute, then turn over and cook the other side. Make 4 pancakes.

Put the plums in a saucepan and add the reserved blackcurrant juice and cinnamon. Cover and cook gently for about 10 minutes or until the plums are soft. Stir in the drained blackcurrants and leave to cool.

Mix together the cream or curd cheese and yoghurt. Add vanilla essence to taste.

Put the first pancake on a plate and spread with a thin layer of the cheese cream followed by a layer of fruit. Continue in the same way until you have used all the ingredients, ending with a layer of cheese cream and fruit. Chill for 1 hour before cutting into wedges to serve.

GOOSEBERRY & APRICOT GRUNT

SERVES 4

FOR THE CAKE:
A little sunflower oil for greasing
3 egg whites
4 tablespoons runny honey
3 oz (75 g) wholemeal flour
1 teaspoon ground ginger
1 oz (25 g) wholemeal breadcrumbs

FOR THE TOPPING:
8 oz (225 g) gooseberries, topped and tailed
5 fl oz (150 ml) water
1 tablespoon runny honey
12 tinned apricot halves, sliced
10 fl oz (300 ml) fromage frais or set natural yoghurt
2 oz (50 g) unsalted peanuts, chopped
Ground ginger for dusting

- A 'grunt' is apparently an old-English term meaning a baked pudding with plenty of stewed or fresh fruit. You can use any fruit you wish for this pudding. Serve as a dessert or at teatime.

Pre-heat the oven to gas mark 5, 375°C (190°C). Lightly oil an 8 inch (20 cm) sandwich tin and line with greaseproof paper.

Whisk the egg whites until stiff and gradually add the honey, whisking all the time. Using a large metal spoon, fold in the sifted flour, ginger and breadcrumbs. Turn into the sandwich tin. Bake in the oven for 15–20 minutes or until the cake is firm and springy.

Meanwhile, gently cook the gooseberries in the water and honey for 10 minutes until soft. Cool and mix lightly with the apricots. Chill in the refrigerator.

Remove the cake from the oven, cool in the tin for 10 minutes, then remove and finish cooling on a wire rack. To assemble the pudding, pile on the fromage frais or yoghurt, spoon over the chilled fruit, sprinkle with chopped peanuts and dust with ginger.

BAKED APPLE NUTTY MERINGUES

SERVES 4

4 medium Bramley apples, cored but left whole
3 oz (75 g) muesli
Grated rind and juice 1 orange
2 tablespoons runny honey

FOR THE MERINGUE TOPPING:
2 egg whites
3 oz (75 g) muscovado sugar
1 oz (25 g) walnuts, chopped

• This makes a lovely change from the usual baked apple.

Pre-heat the oven to gas mark 4, 350°F (180°C).

Cut the skin of each apple horizontally around its circumference with the point of a sharp knife – this stops it from bursting during cooking.

Mix the muesli with the orange rind and juice and stuff into the apple cavities. Place the apples in a shallow ovenproof dish and pour in ½ inch (1 cm) water. Spoon over the honey. Bake for 35–45 minutes or until tender. Remove from the oven and raise the temperature to gas mark 6, 400°F (200°C).

In a large dry mixing bowl, whisk the egg whites until stiff. Gradually whisk in the sugar. Quickly fold in the walnuts. Spoon a heap of nutty meringue on to each apple and return to the oven for a further 3 minutes or until the meringue is golden-brown. Serve at once.

FRESH FRUIT
& CREAM CHEESE PLATTER

SERVES 4

Selection of fresh seasonal fruit
(such as grapes, oranges, bananas, kiwi fruit, strawberries)
8 oz (225 g) low-fat cream cheese
1 heaped tablespoon muscovado sugar
Few drops vanilla essence

• This recipe is best made in the summer when soft fruits are plentiful and inexpensive to buy. Serve with warm oatcakes or muesli cookies (see page 101).

Wash and prepare the fruit and cut or segment (where appropriate) into bite-sized pieces. Mix the cream cheese with the sugar and add a few drops of vanilla essence. Spoon a portion of flavoured cheese into the centre of each of 4 large plates. Arrange the fruit attractively around the cheese and serve.

TRIFLE DIFFERENT

SERVES 4

2 lb (1 kg) cooking apples, peeled, cored and sliced
5 fl oz (150 ml) cold water
4 tablespoons runny honey
1 tin blackberries in unsweetened juice
8 oz (225 g) wholemeal breadcrumbs
2 oz (50 g) hazelnuts, chopped
1 level tablespoon ground cinnamon
5 fl oz (150 ml) orange juice
10 fl oz (300 ml) natural yoghurt

• I like the sharpness of this fresh, light pudding. However, if you have a sweet tooth, use dessert apples instead of cooking apples.

Put the apples, water and 3 tablespoons of the honey in a saucepan. Cover and simmer until very soft. Stir in the blackberries and leave the mixture to cool.

Spread the breadcrumbs on a baking sheet and toast in the oven at gas mark 7, 425°F (220°C) for 10 minutes. Toast the hazelnuts similarly on a separate baking sheet. Set the toasted nuts aside to cool. Transfer the toasted crumbs to a bowl and stir in the cinnamon and orange juice.

Spoon the apple mixture and breadcrumbs in alternate layers into a large glass dish or small individual dishes or stemmed glasses. Spoon the yoghurt on top, sprinkle with the toasted nuts and drizzle over the remaining 1 tablespoon honey.

GOODIE BOX

TIPS

- Don't skip breakfast.

- Before every meal drink a large glass of water or dilute fresh fruit juice. This will help to fill you up so that you are less likely to overeat.

- Prepare your snack pack just after breakfast when you won't be tempted to binge or overprepare.

- Be adventurous – ring the changes by trying different breads, salad, fillings.

- Eat slowly – allow yourself at least 15 minutes to relax and enjoy your meal.

- Keep salt to a minimum; instead, try flavouring with different herbs and spices.

- Use low-fat dairy products.

- Cut down on meat and include more fish.

- Use meat more as a flavouring than as the main bulk of the meal.

Remember – when preparing your snack pack, keep it high in:

- Raw vegetables and fruit.

- Salad ingredients.

- Wholegrain products, such as pitta bread, baps, granary bread, crispbread; wholemeal pasta, brown rice. These are high in fibre and are also good energy foods.

BRUNCH SCONES

MAKES 4 LARGE SCONES

2 teaspoons curry powder
8 oz (225 g) wholemeal flour, plus extra for dusting
1 teaspoon baking powder
2 oz (50 g) vegetable margarine
About 5 fl oz (150 ml) skimmed milk, plus extra for brushing
1 teaspoon poppy seeds

• These scones take no time at all to make. They're really tasty and very satisfying. Try them with the following filling: low-fat cottage cheese mixed with any chopped fresh fruit (for example, banana or black grapes) layered with crunchy lettuce leaves or mustard and cress. Serve with a small flask of home-made soup (see the recipes on pages 40–50).

Pre-heat the oven to gas mark 7, 425°F (220°C).

In a large mixing bowl sift together the curry powder, flour and baking powder. Using your fingertips, rub in the margarine until the mixture resembles breadcrumbs. Add enough milk to bind and form a soft dough. Turn on to a floured board or work-surface and knead lightly.

Pat out the dough to a thickness of ¾ inch (2 cm) and, using a 4 inch (10 cm) cutter, cut into rounds. Place on a floured baking sheet, brush with milk and sprinkle with poppy seeds. Bake in the oven for 10–15 minutes or until risen and golden-brown.

MUNG BEAN CRUNCH

SERVES 1

2 oz (50 g) beansprouts
1 tomato, chopped
1 pear, cored and chopped
2 tablespoons low-calorie French dressing
Freshly ground black pepper

Toss the ingredients together in the dressing and season well. Pack in an air-tight container.

STUFFED PITTA POCKET

SERVES 1

1 wholemeal pitta bread

FOR THE FILLING:
1 large carrot, grated
1 tablespoon unsalted peanuts, chopped
2 oz (50 g) tinned tuna in brine, drained and flaked
Crisp lettuce, shredded
2 tablespoons low-calorie dressing
1 teaspoon French mustard
Freshly ground black pepper

● Follow this with fresh fruit.

In a bowl mix together the filling ingredients. Slit the pitta bread to form a pocket and pack with the filling.

CUCUMBER CHEESE

SERVES 1

4 oz (100g) low-fat cream cheese
¹/4 cucumber, grated
2 spring onions, chopped
Freshly ground black pepper

● This is delicious with bought or home-made oatcakes (see page 97) or a selection of crispbreads.

Simply mix all the ingredients together and season to taste. Spoon into an air-tight container.

WHOLEGRAIN CHICKEN BUTTY

SERVES 1

2 oz (50 g) cooked chicken, sliced
5 radishes, sliced
Selection crisp salad leaves
2 thick slices granary or wholemeal bread

FOR THE DRESSING:
2 teaspoons horseradish sauce
2 teaspoons low-calorie mayonnaise or *thick natural yoghurt*
Freshly ground black pepper

● This is even more delicious if made with warm granary toast.

In a bowl mix the dressing ingredients and season to taste. Add the chicken and radishes.

Assemble the butty in the usual way, including the salad leaves with the chicken filling.

BUTTY OR BAP FILLINGS

● Low-fat cream cheese with raisins, grated carrot and crisp salad leaves.
● Chopped chicken with sliced banana, wholegrain or French mustard and cos lettuce.
● Smoked mackerel and horseradish with plenty of crisp lettuce and sweetcorn.
● Wholemeal pitta bread lightly spread with peanut butter, stuffed with cucumber, lettuce and sunflower or sesame seeds.

RAW VEGETABLES

- Serve washed, peeled vegetables, cut into thick sticks, with a dip such as hummus or tzatziki (available from the delicatessen sections of good supermarkets).
- Use left-over cooked rice, pasta or potatoes, mixed with chopped raw vegetables, nuts and salad ingredients to create interesting flavours.

OTHER HEALTHY SNACKS

- Cooked pizza cut into squares or wedges.
- Flavoured yoghurt with fresh fruit.
- Fresh fruit with cereal bars.
- Yoghurt drinks.

SNACK-PACK PUDDINGS

Without doubt, the best and easiest pudding is fresh fruit. However, here are some other ideas:
- Yoghurt fruit salad. Simply mix fresh fruit with a little yoghurt and cinnamon.
- Diet fruit yoghurt, mixed with a generous amount of muesli.
- Half a small melon, seeds removed, filled with sliced peaches and sprinkled lightly with ground ginger.
- Dried fruit salad using prunes, apricots, pears, dates and so on. Soak the dried fruit in water and cook gently. Cool and chill in the refrigerator. Serve with oatmeal cookies.
- Stewed apples with blackberries (when in season), sweetened with a little honey and served with an oatbar.
- Fruit smoothies. In a liquidiser simply whizz together soft fruit of your choice and yoghurt. Add a little spice and grated orange rind. Pour into a container and sprinkle with chopped walnuts.

HEARTY EATER OUTLETS

A number of companies are taking part in the Hearty Eater campaign organised by BBC tv's *Bazaar* programme, and you can buy Hearty Eater dishes that are kind to your pocket *and* your health from the following outlets:

A.J.'s FAMILY RESTAURANTS

A1 Northbound, Connington, Peterborough (JA1(M)/B660)
A1 Northbound & Southbound, Stoke Rochford, Nr Grantham
A1 Southbound, Wyboston
A10 Bexwell, Downham Market
A10 Stretham, Ely
A27 Chichester By-pass (Eastbound & Westbound)
A43 Nr Hannington, Kettering
A508 Southbound, Grange Farm Services, Collingtree, Northampton
Ipswich Road, Dedham, Colchester
Hedon Road, Hull
Wragby Road, North Greetwell, Lincoln
Milford Service Area, Newmarket Road, Barton Mills, Bury St Edmunds
Buckingham Road, Deanshanger, Milton Keynes

WESTMORELAND MOTORWAY SERVICE RESTAURANTS

M6 Northbound, Tebay West Motorway Services, Nr Penrith
M6 Junction 38 Services, Old Tebay, Orton, Nr Penrith

GATWICK AIRPORT

J. Lyons Catering
South Terminal: Country Table and Airside Buffet
North Terminal: Atlas Restaurant and Voyager's Restaurant

GRANADA SERVICE AREA RESTAURANTS

M1 (Toddington) (J11/12)
M1 Trowell (J25/26)
M1 Woolley Edge (J38/39)
M4 Heston (J2/3)
M4/A34 Newbury (Chieveley)) (on J13)
M4 Leigh Delamere (J17/18)
M5 Frankley (J3/4)
M5 Exeter (on J30)
M6 Burton (J35/36)
M6 Southwaite (J41/42)
M9/M80 Stirling (on J9)
M62 Birch (J18/19)
M62/A1 Ferrybridge (on J33)
M90 Kinross (on J6)
A1(M) Washington
A1(M)/A614 Blyth
A40 Monmouth
A36/A350 Warminster
A38 By-pass Saltash
M1/A50 Leicester (Markfield)
A1 Edinburgh (Musselburgh)
A1 Grantham
A630/A6102 Sheffield
A38/A61 Swanwick

RANK MOTORWAY SERVICES

M2 Farthing Corner (J4/5)
M4 Aust (J21 at the Severn Bridge)
M4 Cardiff West (J33)
M6 Hilton Park (J10/11)
M6 Knutsford (J18/19)
M6 Forton (J32/33)
M61 Anderton (J6/8)
A1(M) Scotch Corner

ROADCHEF SERVICE AREA RESTAURANTS

M4, Pont Abraham
M5 Southbound, Sedgemoor
M5 Southbound, Taunton Deane
M6 Northbound, Sandbach
M6 Southbound, Killington Lake
M8, Harthill
M27 Southbound, Rownhams
M74 Southbound, Bothwell
M74 Northbound, Hamilton
A45 North, Nene Valley
A435/438 Roundabout, Teddington Hands
Caledonia Centre, Glasgow Central Station

SEALINK BRITISH FERRIES

Hearty Eater dishes are available on all Sealink routes.

TRAVELLERS FARE LTD

Hearty Eater dishes are available from some 240 Travellers Fare restaurants at British Rail stations up and down the country.

WELCOME BREAK MOTORWAY RESTAURANTS

M1 Scratchwood (J3/4)
M1 Newport Pagnell (J14/15)
M1 Leicester Forest East (J21/22)
M1 Woodall (J30/31)
M3 Fleet (J4/5)
M4 Membury (J14/15)
M4 Sarn Park (J36)
M5 Michaelwood (J13/14)
M5 Gordano (J19)
M5 Sedgemoor (J21/22)
M6 Corley (J3/4)
M6 Keele (J15/16)
M6 Charnock Richard (J27/28)
M23/A23 Pease Pottage
M25/A1 South Mimms
M62 Burtonwood (J8/9)
M62 Hartshead Moor (J25/26)
A1 Grantham
A12/A45 Copdock Mill
Junction A34/Woodstock Road, Oxford
A34 Sutton Scotney
A74 Gretna Green
A449 Ross Spur

INDEX OF RECIPES

Apple:
  Apple, honey and banana bread
    pudding 113
  Baked apple nutty meringues 116
  Apricot soufflé, hot 110
  Apricot yoghurt ice-cream 106

Baked bean soup, spicy 45
Beef:
  Beef and mushroom loaf with old-
    fashioned red cabbage 54
  Chinese beef noodles 53
Brunch scones 119
Butty or bap fillings 121

Carrot cream 82
Carrot and ginger pudding with
  orange sauce 108
Chapati 100
Chicken:
  Chicken and apple crumble 60
  Chicken and dill paella 66
  Chicken salad pancakes 61
  Chicken and vegetable roast with
    red pepper gravy 64
  Chunky chicken and apple broth 50
  Mustard chicken and bean flan with
    chilli sauce 63
  Peasant chicken 62
  Warm salad with chicken livers and
    apples 85
  Wholegrain chicken butty 121
Chilli sauce 63, 70
Chowder bake 73
Corn cakes 78
Courgette and nut roast with
  carrot cream 82
Couscous warmer 84
Cracked wheat fish crumble 72
Cracked wheat salad with
  mustard dressing 89
Cucumber cheese 120

Fish:
  Baked fish potatoes with spinach
    and sunflower salad 69
  Cracked wheat fish crumble 72
  Fish in oatmeal with hot cucumber
    71
Fruit See also individual names
  Fresh fruit and cream cheese platter
    116
  Fresh fruit rice pudding 111
  Fruit kebabs 110
  Seedy fruit crumble 107

Gooseberry and apricot grunt
  115

Ham and leek gougère 56
Hazelnut bubble and squeak 75
Herb and poppy oatcakes 97

Kebabs 80, 110
Kedgeree pie 74

Lamb and butterbean casserole
  59
Lasagne:
  Green cheese lasagne 76
Leek, carrot and oatmeal soup
  42
Lemon and coriander kebabs 80
Lentil:
  Spiced lentil hotpot 44

Ma's throw-it-together pud 105
Marrow, pea and paprika soup 48
Muesli cake 103
Muesli cookies 101
Muffins 99
Mung bean crunch 119
Mushroom, thyme and brown
  bread soup 46
Mustard bread 49

Mustard celery gannet 94
Mustard chicken and bean flan
  with chilli sauce 63
Mustard dressing 89

Oatcakes 97
Oatmeal flummery 112

Paella 66
Pancakes:
  Chicken salad pancakes 61
Pasta:
  Pasta bows with cauliflower and
    bacon 57
  Pasta soup 41
  Pasta, spinach and tuna salad with
    tomato dressing 86
  Pasta twists with pumpkin and
    green beans 77
  Tuscany pasta 70
Pastry:
  Wholemeal shortcrust pastry 63
Pear and muscovado flan 106
Pitta pocket, stuffed 120
Pizza salad 90
Plum and blackcurrant pancake
  pie 114
Plum Brown Betty 112
Plum pizza, spiced 109
Pork:
  Hungarian pork 58
Potato:
  Baked fish potatoes with spinach
    and sunflower salad 69
  Hazelnut bubble and squeak 75
  Potato, bacon and garlic chowder
    43
  Sweet and spiced potato salad 87

Prune scones 102
Pumpkin:
  Pasta twists with pumpkin and
    green beans 77
  Pumpkin and nutmeg broth 47

Raita 79
Ratatouille with corn cakes 78
Red cabbage 54
Red pepper gravy 65
Rice, lentil and chilli salad 88
Rice pudding with fresh fruit 111

Sage and mushroom muffins 99
Savoy cabbage and onion soup
  with mustard bread 49
Scones 102, 119
Seedy biscuits 100
Seedy bread 96
Snack-pack puddings 122
Spinach and sunflower salad 69
Spring onion Swiss roll 95

Taco salad, hot 91
Thyme bread, Italian 98
Tomato:
  Peasant baked tomatoes 83
  Tomato dressing 86
Trifle different 117
Turkey and chestnut pie 68
Turkey, orange and thyme
  parcels 67

Vegetable curry with raita 79
Vegetables, raw 122

Wholemeal prune scones 102
Wholemeal shortcrust pastry 63